Raintree Steck-Vaughn

Illustrated
SCIENCE
ENCYCLOPEDIA

Volume
11

IMP – LEE

RSVP
RAINTREE
STECK-VAUGHN
P U B L I S H E R S
The Steck-Vaughn Company

Austin, Texas

Published by Raintree Steck-Vaughn Publishers, an imprint of
Steck-Vaughn Company.

Executive Editor	Diane Sharpe
Senior Editor	Anne Souby
Design Manager	Joyce Spicer

This edition edited and designed by Andromeda Oxford Ltd.

Andromeda Editorial and Design

Project Manager	Julia Roles
Editorial Manager	Jenny Fry
Design	TT Designs, T&S Truscott
Cover Design	John Barker

Library of Congress Cataloging-in-Publication Data
Raintree Steck-Vaughn illustrated science encyclopedia.
        p.   cm.
    Includes bibliographical references and index.
    Summary: A twenty-four volume set containing brief articles
on science topics.
    ISBN 0-8172-3943-X (set)
    ISBN 0-8172-3929-4 (Volume 11)
    1. Science—Encyclopedias, Juvenile.   [1. Science—
Encyclopedias.]   I. Raintree Steck-Vaughn Publishers.
Q121.R354   1997
503—dc20   96-11078
                                            CIP
                                            AC

Printed and Bound in the United States of America.
1 2 3 4 5 6 7 8 9 10 IP 00 99 98 97 96

USING THE RAINTREE STECK-VAUGHN ILLUSTRATED SCIENCE ENCYCLOPEDIA

You are living in a world in which science, technology, and nature are very important. You see something about science almost every day. It might be on television, in the newspaper, in a book at school, or some other place. Often, you want more information about what you see.

The *Raintree Steck-Vaughn Illustrated Science Encyclopedia* will help you find what you want to know. It contains information on many science subjects. You may want to find out about computers, the environment, space exploration, biology, agriculture, or mathematics, for example. They are all in the *Raintree Steck-Vaughn Illustrated Science Encyclopedia*. There are many, many other subjects covered as well.

There are twenty-four volumes in the encyclopedia. The articles, which are called entries, are in alphabetical order through the first twenty-two volumes. On the spine of each volume, below the volume number, are some letters. The letters above the line are the first three letters of the first entry in that volume. The letters below the line are the first three letters of the last entry in that volume. In Volume 1, for example, you see that the first entry begins with **AAR** and that the last entry begins with **ANT**. Using the letters makes it easy to find the volume you need.

In Volume 23, there are three special features—reference charts and tables, a bibliography, and an index. In Volume 24, there are interesting projects that you can do on your own. The projects are fun to do, and they help you discover and understand important science principles. Many can give you ideas that can help you develop your own science fair projects.

Main Entries There are two kinds of main entries in the *Raintree Steck-Vaughn Illustrated Science Encyclopedia*. Many of the entries are major topics that are spread over several pages. The titles of these entries are shown at the top of the page in a yellow box. Other entries required less space to cover the topic fully. The titles of these main entries are printed in capital letters. They look like this: **ABALONE**. At the beginning of some entries, you will see a phonetic pronunciation of the entry title, such as (ăb′ ə lō′ nē).

In the front of each volume, there is a pronunciation key. Use it the same way you use your dictionary's pronunciation key.

Cross-References Within the main entries are cross-references referring to other entries in the encyclopedia. Within an entry, they look like this: (see MAMMAL). At the end of an entry, they look like this: *See also* HYENA. These cross-references tell you where to find other helpful information on the subject you are reading about.

Projects At the end of some entries, you will see this symbol: ⚡ PROJECT 1. It tells you which projects related to that entry are in Volume 24.

Illustrations There are thousands of photographs, drawings, graphs, diagrams, tables, and other illustrations in the *Raintree Steck-Vaughn Illustrated Science Encyclopedia*. They will help you better understand the entries you read. Captions describe the illustrations. Many of the illustrations also have labels that point out important parts.

Activities Some main entries include activities presented in a special box. These activities are short projects that give you a chance to work with science on your own.

Index In Volume 23, the index lists every main entry by volume and page number. Many subjects that are not main entries are also listed in the index, as well as the illustrations, projects, activities, and reference charts and tables.

Bibliography In Volume 23, there is also a bibliography for students. The books in this list are on a variety of topics and can supplement what you have learned in the *Raintree Steck-Vaughn Illustrated Science Encyclopedia*.

The *Raintree Steck-Vaughn Illustrated Science Encyclopedia* was designed especially for you, the student. It is a source of knowledge for the world of science, technology, and nature. Enjoy it!

PRONUNCIATION KEY

Each symbol has the same sound as the darker letters in the sample words.

ə	balloon, ago	îr	deer, pier	r	root, tire
ă	map, have	j	join, germ	s	so, press
ā	day, made	k	king, ask	sh	shoot, machine
âr	care, bear	l	let, cool	t	to, stand
ä	father, car	m	man, same	th	thin, death
b	ball, rib	n	no, turn	*th*	then, this
ch	choose, nature	ng	bring, long	ŭ	up, cut
d	did, add	ŏ	odd, pot	ûr	urge, hurt
ĕ	bell, get	ō	cone, know	v	view, give
ē	sweet, easy	ô	all, saw	w	wood, glowing
f	fan, soft	oi	boy, boil	y	yes, year
g	good, big	ou	now, loud	z	zero, raise
h	hurt, ahead	o͝o	good, took	zh	leisure, vision
ĭ	rip, ill	o͞o	boot, noon	'	strong accent
ī	side, sky	p	part, scrap	ˌ	weak accent

GUIDE TO MEASUREMENT ABBREVIATIONS

All measurements in the *Raintree Steck-Vaughn Illustrated Science Encyclopedia* are given in both the customary system and the metric system [in brackets like these]. Following are the abbreviations used for various units of measure.

Customary Units of Measure

mi. = miles	cu. yd. = cubic yards
m.p.h. = miles per hour	cu. ft. = cubic feet
yd. = yards	cu. in. = cubic inches
ft. = feet	gal. = gallons
in. = inches	pt. = pints
sq. mi. = square miles	qt. = quarts
sq. yd. = square yards	lb. = pounds
sq. ft. = square feet	oz. = ounces
sq. in. = square inches	fl. oz. = fluid ounces
cu. mi. = cubic miles	°F = degrees Fahrenheit

Metric Units of Measure

km = kilometers	cu. km = cubic kilometers
kph = kilometers per hour	cu. m = cubic meters
m = meters	cu. cm = cubic centimeters
cm = centimeters	ml = milliliters
mm = millimeters	kg = kilograms
sq. km = square kilometers	g = grams
sq. m = square meters	mg = milligrams
sq. cm = square centimeters	°C = degrees Celsius

For information on how to convert customary measurements to metric measurements, see the Metric Conversions table in Volume 23.

IMPACT Impact, in mechanics, is the striking of one body against another. In an automobile crash, impact happens at the moment of collision between the auto and another object. A law involving impact states that the total momentum (velocity times mass) of the bodies is the same before and after impact if both objects are elastic and not affected by other forces (see ELASTICITY; MASS; MOMENTUM; VOLUME).

In actual practice, some of the energy of momentum is absorbed when a permanent change is caused in one or both of the bodies. The denting that occurs when two autos collide is an example of this. Since the mass of both bodies remains the same, the impact must result in a loss of velocity. The ratio between the differences of the velocities of the two bodies after impact to the same differences before impact is called the impact coefficient.

PROJECT 13

IMPACT

In an automobile accident, impact occurs at the moment a car crashes into something, such as another vehicle or a tree.

IMPALA The impala is an African antelope known for its tremendous jumping ability. High jumps of more than 10 ft. [3 m] and long jumps of 30 ft. [9 m] have been recorded. Impalas are also swift runners. Impalas may run as fast as 50 m.p.h. [80 kph].

Standing from 33 to 40 in. [84 to 101 cm] at the shoulder, impalas weigh from 100 to 180 lb. [45 to 82 kg]. These animals have glossy, reddish brown coats on the top and sides. The underparts are white. The male has a pair of slender horns up to 3 ft. [91 cm] in length. The strongest males gather

IMPALA

The impala is an African antelope noted for its long, curved horns and its ability to leap into the air.

harem herds around them in the breeding season. These herds are made up of females and young. The other males live alone or stay together in bachelor herds.

Impalas live in many areas of eastern and southern Africa. They prefer bush country, where there is plenty of shelter, and rarely venture far from water. Impalas feed mainly on grass, leaves, and fruit. Their natural enemies include leopards, lions, and wild dogs.

See also ANTELOPE.

IMPEDANCE Impedance is a measure of the opposition that a circuit or part of a circuit presents to an alternating electric current. Suppose that a battery is connected to an electric circuit. The battery causes a potential difference to be set up between the two ends of the circuit (see POTENTIAL). This produces a current in the circuit. The size of the current depends on the size of the potential difference. It also depends on the components in the circuit and the wire connecting the components. The wire and components always oppose the flow of current. If the current is a direct current, then the current flows in one direction only (see DIRECT CURRENT). The opposition of a component or a wire to the direct current running through it is called resistance (see RESISTANCE, ELECTRICAL). If the current is an alternating current, its direction reverses at short intervals (see ALTERNATING CURRENT). The opposition to the flow of alternating current includes not only the resistance of the components of the circuit but also the slowdown in movement of charged particles caused by the changing electromagnetic field (see ELECTROMAGNETIC RADIATION). These two factors contribute to impedance.

See also CIRCUIT, ELECTRIC; CURRENT, ELECTRIC.

IMPLANTATION

Implantation is the process in most mammals by which a fertilized egg, or zygote, attaches itself to the uterine wall (see FERTILIZATION; UTERUS). The wall of the uterus prepares for the arrival of the fertilized egg by becoming thicker and developing extra blood vessels (see MENSTRUAL CYCLE). These changes take place because of the action of the female sex hormones estrogen and progesterone (see HORMONE).

When the fertilized egg touches the uterine wall, the egg becomes embedded in the thickened tissue and gradually develops into an embryo.

The term *implantation* is also used to describe the

Egg is fertilized

Fertilized egg begins to divide

Egg is implanted in wall of uterus

IMPLANTATION

Implantation occurs when a fertilized egg—divided into a ball of cells—attaches to the wall of the uterus.

surgical insertion of a mechanical device or an artificial organ into the body of a living organism.

See also PREGNANCY; REPRODUCTIVE SYSTEM; TRANSPLANTATION.

IMPLOSION

An implosion occurs when a vessel (container) collapses inward. It is the reverse of an explosion. An implosion is caused by a difference in the air pressure inside and outside the vessel (see AIR). Normally, the air pushes against both the inside and outside walls of an open vessel with equal pressure. If, however, the vessel is connected to a pump and the air inside the vessel is gradually pumped out, the internal pressure will decrease. Eventually, the pressure outside the vessel will be so great compared with the pressure inside the vessel that the vessel collapses inward, or implodes.

A cathode-ray tube used in electronics contains a partial vacuum. If the tube becomes cracked, it usually implodes with great violence. The cracking weakens the wall of the tube, and the external pressure causes it to implode.

INCANDESCENCE

(ĭn′ kən dĕs′ əns) Incandescence is the emission of visible light by an object at high temperature. An object being heated starts to become incandescent when it gives off red light. As the object becomes hotter, its color changes until white light is given off. The color is a good indication of the temperature. Red light indicates a lower temperature; white light indicates a higher temperature. Most artificial lighting in homes and offices is incandescent. In 1879, the

INCANDESCENCE

The electric light bulb on the left produces all its light by incandescence. Electric current flowing in the thin wire of the filament heats it until it is white hot and gives off light. The bulb on the right produces even more light because the inside of the glass is coated with phosphors—substances that produce white light when illuminated by other light.

first electric light bulbs using the principle of incandescence were produced.

See also ELECTRIC LIGHT; FLUORESCENCE; LUMINESCENCE.

INCLINED PLANE

An inclined plane is a sloping ramp. It is a simple machine and can be used to do work (to lift a load, for example) and to make work easier. An example of an inclined plane is a board sloping from the back of a truck to the ground. To lift a heavy object from the ground to the truck can be difficult. It is usually easier to push the heavy object up the inclined plane. The gentler the slope, the less effort is needed. However, the object must travel a greater distance if it is pushed up the slope than if it is lifted directly up to the truck. The mechanical advantage (MA) of an inclined plane L units long and h units high is L divided by h (in mathematical terms, $MA = L/h$). If an inclined plane is twice as long as it is high, ignoring friction, it only takes half the effort to push an object to the top of the slope as to lift it directly up. Much of the effort in pushing an object along an inclined plane goes into overcoming friction (see FRICTION).

See also MACHINE, SIMPLE. **PROJECT 36, 50**

INCLINED PLANE

It takes less effort to push a load up an inclined plane than to lift it to the same height. Ancient builders used inclined planes to lift heavy blocks of stone.

INCUBATOR

An incubator is a device that maintains a level of temperature and humidity to encourage the growth and development of any living thing that is put inside it. There are many different types of incubators.

Incubators for premature babies look like enclosed cribs with see-through covers. The baby lives inside the incubator until it has grown strong enough to live in a normal environment. Inside the incubator the temperature is controlled by a temperature-sensing device attached to the baby's skin and is adjusted to maintain the baby's body temperature between 97.7°F and 99.5°F [36.5°C and 37.5°C]. Extra oxygen can be added to the incubator to help the baby breathe. In addition, devices that can change the humidity of the enclosed air space may be used (see HUMIDITY).

Incubators for hatching eggs can range from small boxes for hatching just a few eggs to huge commercial units that can hold thousands of eggs. Inside the incubator the temperature is maintained at around 99.5°F [37.5°C]. Moisture is added to keep the relative humidity at around 60 to 65 percent. The ventilation is adjusted to bring in fresh air and remove carbon dioxide.

INDEHISCENCE

(ĭn′ dĭ hĭs′ əns) The term *indehiscence* refers to the inability of certain fruits, such as acorns and hazelnuts, to split open when they are mature to release their seeds. The fruits of

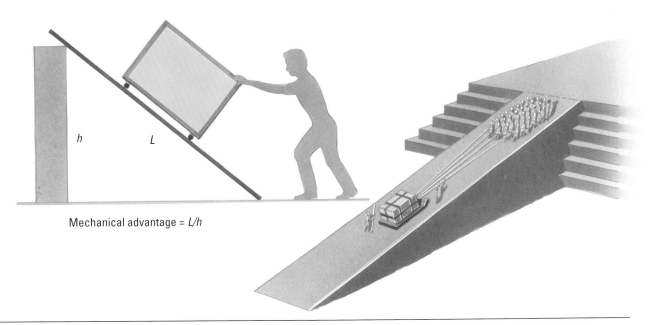

Mechanical advantage = L/h

Dry fruits carried by animals

Hazelnut Wheat Carrot

Fig Blackberry Plum

**Seeds dispersed
by animals that
eat the fruits**

Dry fruits carried by the wind

Maple

Shepherd's
purse

INDEHISCENCE

Seeds from indehiscent fruits are scattered by various
means, often involving animals or the wind.

indehiscent plants are dispersed by air, water, or
animals. For example, many nuts are collected and
buried by small animals, but are never retrieved.
The seed inside an indehiscent fruit eventually ger-
minates and the seedling forces its way through the
fruit wall. Berries and other juicy fruits are also
indehiscent fruits whose seeds are released when
the flesh is eaten by birds.

See also DEHISCENCE; DISPERSION OF PLANTS;
FRUIT; SEED.

INDICATOR Indicators are substances that
show the presence or absence of certain chemicals,
particularly acids and bases, in a solution (see
ACID; BASE; PH). The most common kind of indicator is a dye that changes color over a range of pH.
An example is a purple dye called litmus (see
LITMUS). Litmus is red in an acidic solution and

blue or deep purple in a basic solution. Suppose
that a few drops of litmus are added to a basic solution. The litmus turns the solution purple. Then,
an acidic solution is slowly added to the litmus-
dyed basic solution. When enough acid has been
added, the litmus reacts with the acid, turning the
solution reddish.

All indicators react with the chemicals being
tested. Litmus reacts with a base to form a blue dye
and with an acid to form a red dye. When the acid
is added to the base, they immediately react
together. Eventually, the base is neutralized by the
acid. When a little extra acid is added, it reacts with
the litmus. Therefore, the color of the solution
changes from blue to red. Litmus changes color
over a wide range of pH. Other indicators change
color over smaller ranges of pH. A mixture of such
indicators is called a universal indicator. A universal indicator changes color throughout the pH
scale. Such an indicator can be used to make a
quick, rough guess of the pH of a solution.

A different kind of indicator is the precipitation
indicator. Some chemical reactions cause a precipitate
(solid) to form from a solution (see PRECIPITATE). A
precipitation indicator shows the presence of such a
solid, indicating that the reaction is complete.

Indicators are also used in oxidation-reduction

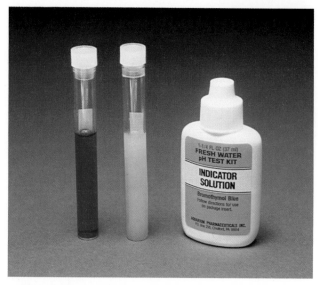

INDICATOR

Some substances, called indicators, change color depending
on the presence or absence of certain chemicals in a
solution. With the type of indicator pictured, a blue color
shows that a solution is basic, while yellow shows that a
solution is acidic.

reactions (see OXIDATION AND REDUCTION). They are called oxidation-reduction indicators, or redox indicators. A redox indicator is one color when it is oxidized and a different color when it is reduced.

🔬 **PROJECT 1**

INDIGO Indigo is a deep blue dye used to color cotton and wool (see DYE). The pigment (coloring substance) in indigo is called indigotin. This dye was once obtained from several plants, especially the indigo plant. The indigo plant, which grows chiefly in India, is a member of the pea family. Indigo is now made artificially.

INDIGO

Indigo is an Asian plant. It was once grown for its leaves, which contain a deep blue dye, also called indigo.

INDUCTION Induction is a phenomenon in physics that occurs when a changing magnetic field causes an electric current to be produced in a wire. This phenomenon is referred to as electromagnetic induction. Electromagnetic induction was first discovered by an English scientist, Michael Faraday, in the early 1800s (see FARADAY, MICHAEL). Faraday placed some wire between the poles of a magnet. Then he joined the ends of the wire through an instrument that could detect an electric current. When the wire was moved through the magnetic field, a direct current flowed through the wire (see DIRECT CURRENT).

Faraday also discovered a similar effect with alternating current (see ALTERNATING CURRENT). He placed two coils of wire near each other. Then he passed an alternating current through one of the coils. An alternating current reverses its flow at

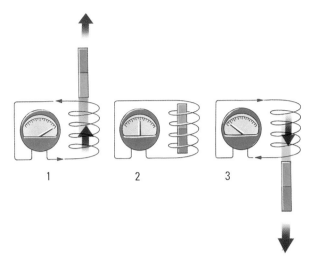

INDUCTION

Electromagnetic induction is shown above. (1) Moving a magnet through a coil induces a current in the coil. (2) If the magnet stops moving, there is no induced current. (3) If the magnet moves in the opposite direction, the direction of the current flow is reversed.

short intervals. Because the current is changing, it sets up a changing magnetic field around itself. This field changes with the current. Faraday found that a similar current was induced in the second coil. It was induced by the changing magnetic field.

This second type of electromagnetic induction is used in transformers (see TRANSFORMER). Transformers are used to change high voltages to lower ones, and vice versa. In a transformer, the voltage in one coil is used to induce a voltage in the other. The size of the induced voltage depends on the number of turns of wire in each coil.

See also ELECTROMAGNETISM.

INDUCTION (LOGICAL) Induction is a method of investigation used by scientists. When scientists perform experiments, they make observations. They then try to explain the results of their observations with a theory. Then they, or other scientists, perform more experiments to test the theory. This method of investigating the world—reasoning from particular cases to general conclusions—is called induction. It is the opposite of deduction. In deduction, scientists start with a theory. Then they perform experiments to confirm that the theory is accurate—drawing a particular truth from a more general one.

See also SCIENCE.

INDUSTRY

An industry is a group of businesses or companies that provide a similar product or service. There are many different types of industries. Some change a raw material into a product. For example, the petroleum refining industry produces products such as lubricating oils, gasoline, and other fuels from crude oil. Other industries, such as the shipping and transportation industries, move goods from place to place. Service industries, such as the banking, health care, and communications industries, provide the services needed by modern society.

For simplicity, industries are often classified into nine major divisions according to the main raw materials and types of products they produce. These are (1) agriculture, hunting, forestry, and fishing; (2) mining and quarrying; (3) manufacturing; (4) electricity, gas, and water; (5) construction, wholesale and retail trade, and restaurants and hotels; (6) transportation, storage, and communication; (7) finance, insurance, property, and business services; (8) community, social, and personal services; and (9) other industries.

In all industries there are certain inputs and outputs. Inputs include the machinery and raw materials used. Outputs are the products or services that an industry produces. Five basic inputs are necessary to produce goods and services. These are natural resources and raw materials, capital, labor, management, and technology. Natural resources are renewable or nonrenewable (see NATURAL RESOURCES). Renewable resources, such as fish and forests, will never run out if they are properly

MANUFACTURING AND CONSTRUCTION
The aerospace industry (far left) includes the manufacture of aircraft and rockets. The machine (left) is driving piles into the ground to form the foundation for constructing a large building. Most countries with navies have a shipbuilding industry (below).

managed. Nonrenewable resources, such as mineral deposits and hydrocarbons like oil and gas, exist only in limited amounts. Capital includes all the money an industry needs to run its business, as well as the buildings, machinery, and tools used in its work. Labor is the work that people do to produce goods and services. Management is the people who make business decisions for industry. Technology involves using all available knowledge to develop the best system to produce goods in the most efficient way.

Industry provides us with all our basic needs for food, clothing, and shelter, and makes our lives more pleasant by providing things such as entertainment, medicines, and labor-saving devices. However, industry also has some harmful side effects. One of the greatest is the damage some industries cause to the environment by pollution (see POLLUTION). Another is its potential to use up the supply of nonrenewable raw materials and energy resources. To fight pollution, industries can install systems that remove harmful pollutants from their waste products. They can also work to develop production methods that create fewer harmful waste products in the first place, and look for ways to make useful products from the waste they produce.

It is important to remember that fighting pollution costs industry money because it uses resources such as capital, labor, management, and technology. Reducing pollution may mean that customers will have to pay higher prices for the goods and services they buy from industry, and that industry will have to accept lower profits from the goods it produces. These choices are difficult because industry needs to make some profit so that it has money to invest in developing new, more efficient and more environmentally friendly production methods. On the other hand, if customers refuse to accept higher prices, industrial profits could drop.

Industry uses huge amounts of energy to produce goods (see ENERGY). Today most energy is generated from nonrenewable natural resources such as coal, gas, and oil. To encourage industries to make the most efficient use of energy, many people believe that the cost of energy should be allowed to rise. Higher prices would encourage industries to make more efficient use of power and encourage them to work to develop alternative sources of energy.

CERAMICS AND TEXTILES

These plates (above) are being made by a process called dust pressing. Granules of dry clay are compressed in a mold in the form of a plate, which does not need drying before being fired (baked in an oven). Making pottery is an important part of the ceramics industry. The manufacture of textiles is also a major industry. Lengths of cloth (left) are dyed after having been woven.

971

INERT GAS
A scientist in Antarctica releases a weather balloon filled with helium, one of the inert gases.

INERT GAS An inert, or noble, gas is any one of six elements in group 0 of the periodic table of the elements (see PERIODIC TABLE, VOL. 23). Unlike most gases, they exist as single atoms, and not as molecules consisting of two or more atoms. The six inert gases are argon (Ar), helium (He), krypton (Kr), neon (Ne), radon (Rn), and xenon (Xe). They do not react readily with other elements because it is extremely difficult to add or remove electrons from their atoms in order to form a chemical bond. This is why they were at first called the inert gases. But in the 1960s, it was found that radon, krypton, and xenon could combine with fluorine and oxygen under some conditions.

The inert gases were discovered by the British scientists Lord Rayleigh and William Ramsay in the late 1890s (see RAMSAY, SIR WILLIAM). Argon was the first one to be identified. It was found when the scientists noticed that there was always a small amount of another gas left when they were examining nitrogen gas from the atmosphere. This proved to be argon. Apart from argon, there are only trace amounts of the other inert gases in the atmosphere.

Argon is used to fill electric light bulbs. Helium is used to lift the scientific balloons that carry instruments high in the earth's atmosphere. Radon is highly radioactive and is used in medicine to treat cancer. Both argon and helium are used for arc welding metals such as aluminum and magnesium. These and other inert gases are used in gas lasers.
See also ARGON; HELIUM; KRYPTON; NEON; RADON.

INERTIA Inertia is the tendency of matter to remain at rest unless acted upon by an outside force. Inertia is also the tendency of a moving body to continue moving at the same speed in the same direction. This tendency was formulated as a scientific law by Sir Isaac Newton in 1687. The law of inertia is known as Newton's first law of motion (see DYNAMICS; NEWTON, SIR ISAAC).

The greater the mass of the matter, the greater its inertia (see MASS). For example, an automobile has greater inertia than a bicycle. It takes more effort to get the automobile moving than it does to get the bicycle moving. Likewise, it takes greater effort to stop an automobile than it does to stop a bicycle. A person riding a bicycle or in an automobile that stops moving suddenly will keep moving forward because of inertia. This is why wearing safety belts when in a car is important to help prevent injuries. PROJECT 32, 46

ACTIVITY *How to show inertia*

Place a coin on a playing card over a glass. Tap the edge of the card sharply. The card will go flying off. The inertia of the coin will prevent it from moving, and it will drop into the glass.

INERTIAL GUIDANCE

Transoceanic air transport planes (above), nuclear submarines, and many missiles and rockets use inertial guidance systems to navigate.

INERTIAL GUIDANCE Inertial guidance is a system of navigating that does not depend on observations of stars, planets, or the sun. It depends only on measurements of amount and direction of accelerations, or changes in velocity (see ACCELERATION). It is used mainly in nuclear submarines, missiles, rockets, and transoceanic air transport planes.

Nuclear submarines are able to remain submerged for many months without surfacing. By remaining submerged, they reduce the risk of detection. However, they are not able to navigate by conventional methods. A special computer in the inertial guidance system records every change in the ship's speed and direction, the speed of currents under the ocean, and other factors. The computer can determine instantly the exact location of the submarine. Direction-sensing instruments that contain gyroscopes and speed-detecting devices, called accelerometers, feed information to the computer, allowing the computer to pinpoint the submarine's location throughout its course (see GYROSCOPE).

Many missiles and rockets employ a modified version of the submarine inertial guidance system. This system keeps the missile or rocket on a preselected course and automatically makes corrections when the missile or rocket wanders from the desired path.

See also NAVIGATION.

INFECTION Infection is the invasion of the body by organisms called pathogens. Many kinds of bacteria, viruses, and fungi can be pathogens—that is, they can cause infectious disease (see DISEASE; PATHOGEN). The body has defenses against

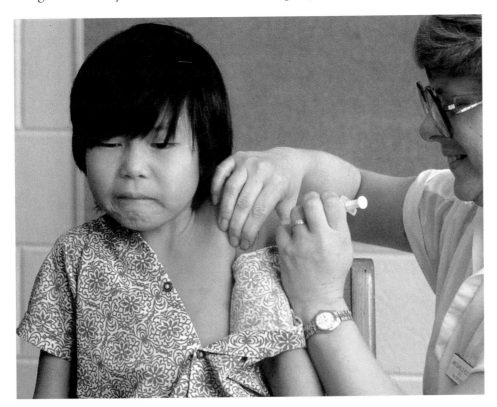

INFECTION

Vaccination is one way of preventing infection. Here, a young girl receives a preschool vaccination at a clinic. The vaccine stimulates her immune system to produce antibodies to fight infection.

infection. The skin forms a strong barrier. Most body openings, such as the ears, nose, and mouth, are lined with membranes that secrete sticky mucus to trap pathogens. Within the body there is a powerful immune system that attacks invading pathogens and neutralizes (makes harmless) their poisons (see IMMUNITY).

Pathogens can enter the body through breaks in the skin caused by injury or surgery. This is why cuts and burns must be kept clean. It is also why surgeons must make sure that their hands, clothes, and instruments are scrubbed clean and sterilized (see ASEPSIS). Biting insects spread a number of diseases by piercing the skin of their victims. Then pathogens carried by the insect or from other sources can enter the body.

Many pathogens infect the body through the stomach and intestines. Such infection may result if a person consumes contaminated food or water. However, common pathogens often are destroyed by the acid in the stomach.

The easiest route into the body for many pathogens is by way of the lungs. A large number of common infectious diseases are spread by people breathing in tiny droplets of pathogen-filled moisture. These droplets are sprayed into the air whenever a person with an infectious disease coughs, sneezes, or simply exhales. Diseases that can spread from one person to another are said to be contagious.

The use of antiseptics and other hygienic measures can reduce the chance of infection (see ANTISEPTIC; HYGIENE). However, some diseases are so contagious that patients must be kept in isolation, or out of contact with other people except medical staff who are immune or specially protected against the disease.

INFINITY Infinity means an unlimited extent of space, time, or quantity. For example, if you start counting the whole numbers from one, you will never reach the end. There is always a number bigger than any number that you can think of. The whole numbers are said to reach infinity. This means that they go on "forever." Infinity is sometimes represented by the symbol ∞.

INFLAMMATION Inflammation is a way in which the body reacts to injury or infection. The injured or infected tissues become inflamed—that is, swollen, reddened, and warm. The inflamed area becomes tender and feels painful. The body temperature and pulse rate may both increase. These changes are the result of chemicals released by white blood cells that are attracted to the site of any tissue injury. These chemicals cause the blood vessels in the area to become dilated (enlarged), increasing the blood flow. They also cause the small blood vessels, called capillaries, to become leaky. This allows fluid from the blood to escape into the surrounding tissue. The fluid presses on nerves, causing pain. However, the net result of all these processes is beneficial, because it helps kill harmful microorganisms and repair the damaged tissues by increasing the blood flow through them and stimulating cells in these tissues to divide and grow. *See also* INFECTION; MIRCOORGANISM.

INFLORESCENCE An inflorescence is a cluster of flowers or a flowerhead all growing from the same plant stem. There are two basic types of inflorescence: determinate inflorescence and indeterminate inflorescence. In a determinate inflorescence, the stem stops growing when flowers develop from

INFLORESCENCE—An umbel

The flower cluster on this geranium is an example of a simple umbel, with a single blossom on the end of each branch of the flower stalk.

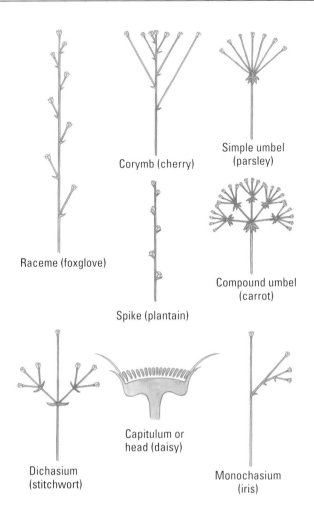

INFLORESCENCE—Types of inflorescence
The above diagrams show the main types of inflorescence, with examples.

buds at the tip of the stem. In an indeterminate inflorescence, the stem continues growing as flowers develop near the tip. As the stem grows, more flowers are produced. As a result, the lower flowers are older than the upper ones. The different shapes within the two main groups depend largely on the lengths and arrangement of the individual flower stalks.

INFLUENZA Influenza, commonly called the flu, is a disease caused by several different kinds of viruses. It is an infectious disease that spreads rapidly from person to person. When a large number of people in the same area are infected with the flu, it is called an epidemic of influenza (see EPI-DEMIC; INFECTION).

The influenza virus settles in the lining of the nose and throat. It causes sneezing, coughing, and

a sore throat. It can also cause fever, sudden chills, and headache. Often, sufferers have aches and pains all over the body. They may feel extremely tired. In most cases, influenza lasts between three days and a week.

Some kinds of influenza are very mild, and the person infected may not even become ill. Others are dangerous. The "Spanish flu" epidemic after World War I (1914–1918) killed more people than were killed in the war itself. Fortunately, there have been no more influenza epidemics as serious as that since. However, because people can travel long distances very rapidly today, influenza epidemics have the potential to spread quickly around the world.

It is possible to prepare vaccines that give protection against viral diseases such as influenza. However, there are so many different kinds of influenza that it is not practical to prepare vaccines against them all. If there seems to be a danger of an epidemic, then a vaccine against a particular kind of influenza can be prepared. The exact type of virus responsible is first identified. Millions of doses must be prepared and distributed to give the population immunity against the disease.
See also IMMUNITY; VACCINATION.

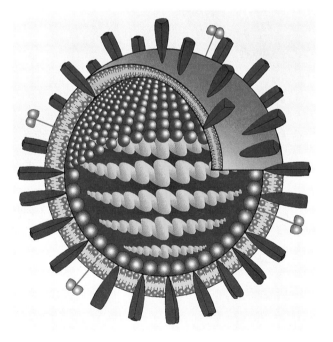

INFLUENZA
This drawing shows the structure of an influenza virus. Its genetic material is a core of RNA (ribonucleic acid), shown in yellow/green in the center. The outer membrane is armed with spikes, which stick to any cell the virus attacks.

INFORMATION TECHNOLOGY

Information technology is the technology used in the field of information science. Information technology includes computer systems and programs, and electronic storage systems, such as magnetic disks and optical discs. Information science deals with what information is and how people use it. It brings together ideas from many areas, including communications, computer technology, information theory, linguistics, management, mathematics, psychology, and other sciences that look at the way people behave.

Information scientists work to develop better ways to produce, store, make available, and use information. Information technology is an essential tool in their work. There are two main focuses in information technology. One is the development of new computer programs and software to make it easier to manage large amounts of information. The other is the development of new devices, or hardware, to store the information.

One of the earliest computer software-based technologies used to improve the transfer of information was the Keyword in Context (KWIC) indexing system. It was developed in 1959 by Hans Peter Luhn and colleagues at IBM. In a KWIC index, a computer was used to generate entries from the words in titles of documents automatically, without the help of a person. The KWIC index was an early example of a computer database. Database programs are an important part of modern information technology. A database is a body of information, usually stored on a computer, that can be searched and handled.

A computer network consists of several computers located in different places linked together, usually by telephone lines. The growth of computer networks means that it is now possible to search information stored on different computers and combine it to form a single database. Computer networks also make it possible for people to gain access to a wide range of information resources and databases using computers at home or at school. The largest of these networks is the Internet. It is maintained by the National Science Foundation and connects computers all over the world.

The information available on computer databases is stored on devices, or media, such as magnetic disks. This "hardware" can be connected, or interfaced, with computers. Information is stored on magnetic disks by polarizing magnetic particles in one of two directions. The computer reads the polarized particles as a code consisting of strings of

OFFICE COMPUTERS

The personal computers (PCs) on each desk of a modern office (right) are linked together in a network. In this way, they can all have access to such devices as a scanner (for taking in pictures) and a laser printer (for printing out text and pictures).

CD-ROM INFORMATION

A single CD-ROM can hold a complete encyclopedia, including its text (words) and all of its pictures. CD-ROMs can be looked at on a TV-type computer screen (left).

zeroes and ones, referred to as bytes (see BYTE).

The information on the disks is recorded in separate tracks arranged in concentric circles, like the grooves in a record. Magnetic materials make it possible to lay the tracks of information closer together on the disk. Data compression techniques compress, or squeeze, more data onto a single disk, making it possible to store more information than ever before. Nevertheless, information technologists are constantly looking for better ways to store greater amounts of information. Optical discs, also known as laser discs or CD-ROMs (Compact Disc Read-Only Memory), are one of

the most promising technologies (see CD-ROM). These discs record data in the form of pits and bumps on a rapidly rotating disc. Information is retrieved from the disc using a small laser beam to produce a reflection from its surface that can be read by the computer. CD-ROMs offer a convenient way to store, search, and retrieve large amounts of information. Like other types of computer-based information systems, CD-ROMs can be networked, so that information stored on a CD-ROM read by one computer can also be read by someone using another computer on the network.
See also COMPUTER.

INFRARED RAY An infrared ray is a form of electromagnetic radiation that has a longer wavelength than visible light and therefore cannot be seen by the human eye. Infrared rays are part of the electromagnetic spectrum (see ELECTROMAGNETIC RADIATION; SPECTRUM). Infrared rays have a longer wavelength than visible light, but are shorter than other long-wavelength radiation, such as microwaves and radio waves. All objects give off infrared rays according to their temperature. The warmer an object is, the more infrared rays it gives off.

During World War II (1939–1945), an instrument called a sniperscope was used to detect something warmer than its surroundings. This was valuable in finding enemies hiding in the dark or in fog. Infrared rays also have applications in photography and medical treatment. Astronomers make telescopic observations of infrared radiation to learn about planetary atmospheres and to measure temperatures of stars. Infrared rays were discovered by the British astronomer Sir William Herschel in 1800 (see HERSCHEL, SIR WILLIAM).

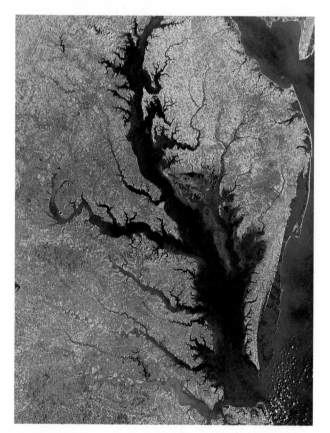

INFRARED RAY

This picture of Chesapeake Bay was taken by a Landsat earth resources satellite using infrared photography.

INGOT An ingot is a mass of metal cast into a size or shape convenient for storing, reshaping, or refining. For example, a gold ingot is often shaped like a bar. Steel ingots range in weight from a few ounces to many tons. In addition to gold and steel, silver and tin are often cast into ingots.
See also METAL AND METALLURGY.

INJECTION In medicine, an injection is the process of forcing a fluid into the body tissues with the use of a syringe or other medical equipment and a hollow needle. In a hypodermic (under the skin) injection, a syringe and a sharp needle are used. The doctor or other health-care professional attaches the needle to the syringe barrel. He or she puts the liquid medicine in the syringe, places the needle into the patient's skin, and presses on the plunger of the syringe (after making sure no air bubbles are trapped in the liquid). This forces the medicine through the needle. There are different types of hypodermic injections. They are named for the tissue into which the injection is made. Intradermal injections are made between the layers of skin. Injections made below the layers of skin are called subcutaneous injections. In an intramuscular injection, the needle penetrates a muscle (see SKIN).

A hypodermic needle can be used to give an intravenous injection. An intravenous injection is one given inside a vein. Doctors use intravenous injections to put needed substances into the bloodstream. When blood, blood plasma, or serum is given this way, it is called a transfusion (see BLOOD; BLOOD TRANSFUSION; SERUM). Patients who cannot eat or drink are kept alive by intravenous feeding of water containing sugar, proteins, fats, vitamins, and minerals.

INORGANIC CHEMISTRY Chemicals are divided into two groups of compounds: organic compounds and inorganic compounds. Organic compounds contain the element carbon. Inorganic compounds, as a general rule, do not contain carbon. Inorganic chemistry is the study of inorganic compounds.
See also CHEMISTRY; COMPOUND; ORGANIC CHEMISTRY.

An insect is any of more than one million species of invertebrate animals belonging to the class Insecta in the phylum Arthropoda (see ARTHROPODA; INVERTEBRATE). Insects live almost everywhere in the world except in the deep seas. They are the most widespread and successful animals that ever lived. The fossil record indicates that insects existed more than 400 million years ago. Since that time, they have consistently been able to adapt quickly and efficiently to changes in climate and other changes in the environment (see ADAPTATION).

The insect body The body of an insect is divided into three sections: the head, the thorax, and the abdomen. The head has one pair of antennae that is used for the senses of touch, taste, and smell (see ANTENNAE). There are usually two compound eyes, which provide good vision, and two or three simple eyes (ocelli), which detect light or darkness (see EYE AND VISION). The mouth may have biting or chewing jaws or may have piercing and sucking structures. The mouths of some insects have spongelike pads for absorbing liquids. The head also contains the brain, to which are attached nerves that run through all parts of the body (see NERVOUS SYSTEM).

The thorax, or middle part of the body, has three pairs of jointed legs (see THORAX). These legs are equipped with sticky pads or claws at the ends. Insects are the only invertebrates with wings. Although most insects have two pairs of wings, some have only one pair. Some insects lack wings altogether. Some wingless insects, such as fleas, have lost their wings during their evolution, but others, such as the bristletails, have never had wings at any point in their evolution (see EVOLUTION).

The abdomen, or end part of the body, contains organs for digestion, excretion, and reproduction (see ABDOMEN). Tiny openings called spiracles on the abdomen and thorax allow air to enter the tracheae, or air tubes. These tubes carry air directly to the tissues in all parts of the body, where oxygen diffuses into the cells and carbon dioxide diffuses from the cells into the air tubes (see DIFFUSION). The abdomen also contains tiny tubes called malpighian tubules. These tubules remove wastes from the blood while recycling most of the water to the body. For this reason, insects can live for long periods of time without water (see EXCRETION). A female insect often has an egg-laying tube called an ovipositor. In some insects, the ovipositor has been modified for use as a stinger.

An insect's body is covered with a tough exoskeleton (see SKELETON). The exoskeleton provides protection from injury and loss of moisture and serves as a place of attachment for muscles. Since the exoskeleton does not increase in size as the insect grows larger, it must be shed several times during an insect's development (see MOLTING).

INSECT ORDERS

Insects make up the animal class Insecta. The class is divided into many orders, and the most important orders are shown here. The biggest order (in terms of numbers of species) is the beetles.

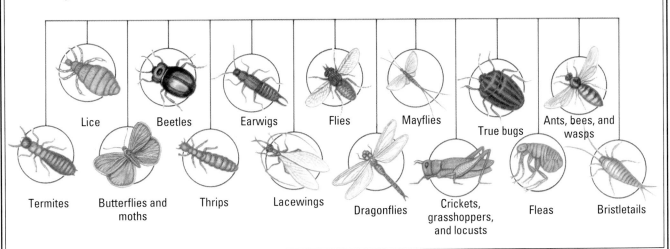

Lice Beetles Earwigs Flies Mayflies True bugs Ants, bees, and wasps

Termites Butterflies and moths Thrips Lacewings Dragonflies Crickets, grasshoppers, and locusts Fleas Bristletails

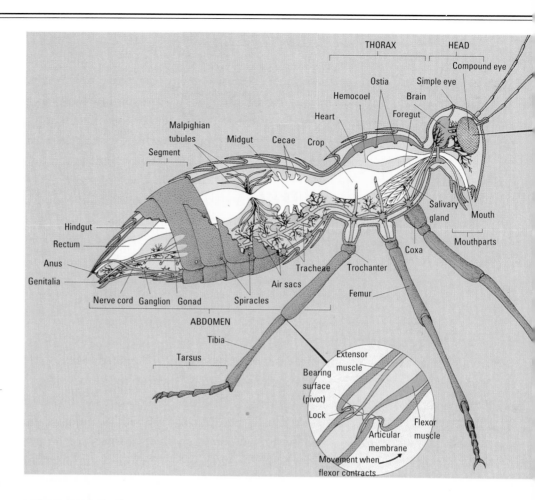

THORAX **HEAD**
Compound eye
Ostia Simple eye
Hemocoel Brain
Heart Foregut
Malpighian
tubules Midgut Cecae Crop
Segment
Salivary
gland Mouth
Hindgut
Rectum Mouthparts
Anus Coxa
Genitalia Tracheae Trochanter
Air sacs Femur
Nerve cord Ganglion Gonad Spiracles
ABDOMEN Tibia
Tarsus Extensor
muscle
Bearing
surface
(pivot)
Lock Flexor
muscle
Articular
membrane
Movement when
flexor contracts

AVOIDING PREDATORS

The so-called wasp beetle
(below) looks like a wasp
and so is left alone by
predators, such as hungry
birds. The grasshopper
(below right) escapes its
enemies by making sudden,
long leaps.

The entire body of an insect is usually covered
with tiny bristles. These bristles are connected to
nerves and are very sensitive to contact. It is for this
reason that an insect can detect even the faintest
breeze or other movement.

Many insects have special hearing organs located
on the abdomen, thorax, or legs. Some of these

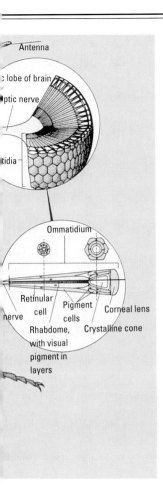

Antenna

c lobe of brain

ptic nerve

tidia

Ommatidium

Retinular
cell
nerve
Pigment
cells
Corneal lens
Rhabdome,
with visual
pigment in
layers
Crystalline cone

INSECT ANATOMY

This cutaway diagram (left) shows the body of a typical insect. There are three main body regions: the head, with antennae, eyes, and mouthparts; the thorax, which usually has two pairs of wings (not shown) and three pairs of legs; and the abdomen, which contains the digestive system and sex organs.

body. As the eggs pass out of the female's body, they are fertilized by the sperm (see FERTILIZATION). The fertilized eggs are usually not tended by the insect but develop near or in a source of nourishment and protection. In some cases, fertilization is external. This means that the female lays the eggs, and then the male fertilizes them. Some insects produce eggs that develop into adults without being fertilized (see PARTHENOGENESIS; REPRODUCTION).

Some primitive insects hatch from their eggs looking just like miniature adults. Most insects, however, go through several stages of development called metamorphosis (see METAMORPHOSIS). In complete metamorphosis, there are four stages of development: egg, larva, pupa, adult. In incomplete metamorphosis, there are three stages: egg, nymph, adult. The nymph looks like a small adult, but it lacks wings and a fully developed reproductive system. As the insect goes through its development, it molts several times. The entire process of metamorphosis may take a few days or several years, depending on the species of insect and on the environmental conditions. Many insects lay eggs that can survive the winter or other unfavorable conditions (see DORMANCY).

INSECT MOUTHPARTS

Insects eat a variety of foods and have mouthparts suited to a particular diet. The mosquito has piercing mouthparts for pushing through an animal's skin and sucking blood. The housefly's mouthparts resemble a sponge, which are used to mop up food previously softened with saliva. The butterfly's long mouthparts uncoil to suck nectar.

organs are spaces covered by a thin membrane that moves with vibrations in the air.

Insect life One reason for the abundance of insects is that they are able to reproduce quickly and in large numbers. Reproduction is usually sexual, with the male inserting sperm into the female's

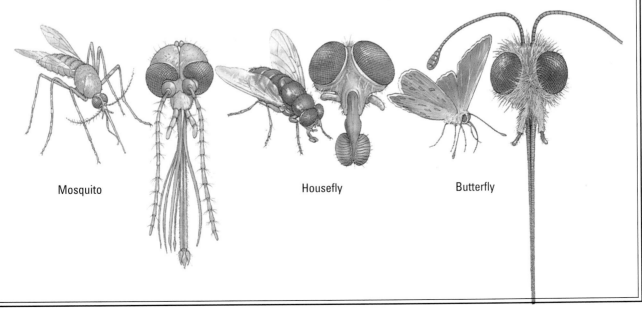

Mosquito

Housefly

Butterfly

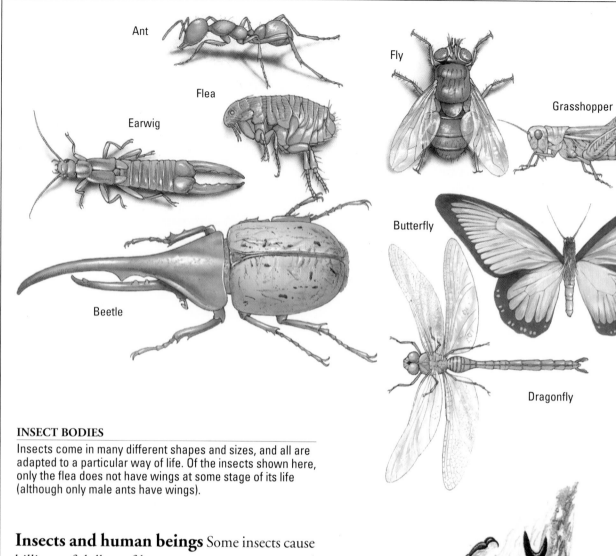

Ant

Flea

Earwig

Fly

Grasshopper

Butterfly

Beetle

Dragonfly

INSECT BODIES

Insects come in many different shapes and sizes, and all are adapted to a particular way of life. Of the insects shown here, only the flea does not have wings at some stage of its life (although only male ants have wings).

Insects and human beings Some insects cause billions of dollars of losses every year to crops and other plants. Some insects bite or sting human beings and other animals. Some of these insects carry disease-causing organisms such as bacteria, fungi, viruses, or wormlike parasites.

Many insects, however, are of vital importance to human beings. They are responsible for most of the pollination of plants (see POLLINATION). Some insects eat weeds or more harmful insects. Some insects make tunnels in the ground that bring air into the soil. Insects are the major source of food for birds, fish, and many other animals. In some countries, insects are used as food for human beings. Some insects feed on dead and decaying material and form a vital link in the food chain (see FOOD CHAIN). Insects also provide silk, honey, and wax. Insects themselves are a source of substances used in dyes, shellacs, medicines, and many other products.

SAP SUCKER

The horned chafer is a type of beetle. It sticks its pointed mouthparts into plants to feed on their sap.

INSECT THREAT

A male stag beetle (right) frightens enemies by waving its large "horns," which give this beetle its name.

BULKY MOTH

The colorful elephant hawk moth (below), seen here on an iris bud, gets its name from its large, heavy body.

Insect control Harmful insects are often controlled by chemicals called insecticides, but many species have become resistant to these chemicals (see INSECTICIDE). As a result, entomologists (scientists who study insects) and other biologists are constantly experimenting with new, safer means of insect control. They have developed methods of introducing predators, parasites, and insect diseases to control insects (see BIOLOGICAL CONTROL). Sterilized males have also been used as a method of controlling insect populations. Large numbers of these males are released in areas where control is desired. They mate with the females, which then lay unfertilized eggs. These eggs fail to develop. Since many harmful insects thrive in organic wastes, they can often be controlled by improving sanitary conditions.

See also ENTOMOLOGY.

PROJECT 65, 66

INSECTICIDE An insecticide is a chemical pesticide used to kill harmful insects (see INSECT; PESTICIDE). The use of insecticides has helped save many crops and ornamental plants that otherwise would have been killed by insects. However, insecticides are dangerous chemicals and should be used with caution. Care must be taken that insecticides are not overused and that insecticide containers are disposed of correctly.

There are some insecticides that are simple compounds found in nature. Most, however, are complex compounds made by humans (see COMPOUND). Insecticides kill insects in one of two ways. Some insecticides are sprayed on an insect's body. The insecticide then interferes with certain body processes, such as respiration. As a result, the insect dies. Other insecticides are sprayed on the plants that insects eat. After eating the sprayed plants, or sucking their sap, the insects die.

Insecticides can sometimes damage the environment. Some insecticide may seep into groundwater (see GROUNDWATER). This is dangerous to humans because this water may be used as drinking water. Insecticide may also be washed by rain into rivers and other bodies of water. In this way, fish and other water animals may be killed. Also, animals such as worms may be accidentally sprayed by an insecticide. This will not kill the worms, but when birds, such as robins, eat the worms, the birds may die. Sometimes, the insecticide is passed along the food chain, becoming more concentrated—and thus, more harmful—as it does so (see FOOD CHAIN). Scientists have found that some birds of prey, such as eagles, ospreys, and falcons, can survive with large amounts of insecticides in their bodies. However, the insecticides cause the shells of the birds' eggs to be very thin and breakable. If the eggs break easily, few young birds will hatch. Partly because of this, eagles, ospreys, and falcons have become rare in some parts of the United States (see ENDANGERED SPECIES). Another problem with many insecticides is that they can stay poisonous for a very long time. This has led to the restricting and even banning of certain insecticides in many countries. DDT is an example of an insecticide that has been banned in the United States.

In recent years, some insects—especially mosquitoes—have developed a resistance to various insecticides. That is, the chemicals no longer kill them. Perhaps only two out of ten thousand mosquitoes will survive a spraying of an insecticide. However, these two mosquitoes may reproduce, and their offspring may inherit the resistance to the insecticide. Because mosquitoes reproduce rapidly, in a short time there may be one thousand mosquitoes that are not killed by the insecticide. In a few years, there may be ten thousand mosquitoes again, all of which can survive being sprayed by the insecticide.

All these problems have led to a decrease in the amount of insecticides used. Other methods, such as biological control, are now used along with insecticides.

See also AGRICULTURE; BIOLOGICAL CONTROL.

INSECTIVORE An insectivore is an organism that eats insects. Most insectivores are animals, but insectivorous plants, such as the Venus's-flytrap, also exist. Insects that land or crawl onto a special leaf of an insectivorous plant are trapped and digested. Insectivorous animals include shrews, moles, bats, and some other mammals. Some of them eat nothing but insects. Others also eat such

INSECTICIDE

This light aircraft is spraying insecticide to kill insects on a crop.

INSECTIVORE

Insectivores are animals that eat mainly insects. They include (1) the common shrew, which finds insects with its long, pointed snout; (2) the common hedgehog; and (3) the leaf-nosed bat, which flies at night, using a type of animal sonar to locate insects in the dark.

animals as worms. Insectivorous mammals usually have sharp teeth in order to kill and chew the insects, which sometimes have tough shells.

See also CARNIVORE; CARNIVOROUS PLANT; HERBIVORE; OMNIVORE; VENUS'S-FLYTRAP.

INSTINCT Instincts are behavior patterns that are inborn and do not have to be learned. An instinctive behavior is inherited, or passed from one generation to the next (see HEREDITY).

For a behavior to be considered instinctive, it must be something that is demonstrated by all of the males, or all of the females, or all of the members of a species. Examples of instinctive behavior are the maternal behavior of a mother toward her young; the reverse response, in which the young follow their mother; the courtship behavior between males and females; and migration from one location to another.

Instinctive behavior begins with a special stimulus, also called a releaser. The stimulus might be a specific color or a particular movement. A certain change in the environment can also serve as a stimulus to some species. Whatever the stimulus, it causes body chemicals called hormones to be released that in turn make the animal carry out its instinctive behavior.

See also BEHAVIOR OF ANIMALS; HORMONE.

INSTINCT

The maternal behavior of many kinds of mother animals toward their babies, such as the mother zebu with her calf above, is instinctive behavior. Instincts are not learned; they are inborn and passed from generation to generation.

INSULATION

Insulation is material that protects against heat, cold, electricity, or sound. Clothing is one of the most common types of insulation. Wool clothes are warmer than those made of most other fabrics. This is because air becomes trapped in the meshes of the wool fiber. This dead (motionless) air does not conduct heat easily and serves as a protective layer between the body and the outside air. This prevents body heat from escaping. Other kinds of insulation do not readily permit electricity or sound to pass through. These include the rubber or other coating that surrounds electrical wires and the soundproofing found in theaters and homes.

Many materials provide protection against heat and cold. The body is protected by clothing made of various textiles. Generally, several layers of light

HEAT INSULATION

A worker unrolls a mat made of glass fibers to insulate a house. The insulation keeps heat from escaping through the ceiling of the rooms below during winter.

ACTIVITY *How to test insulation*

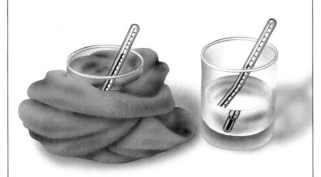

Place thermometers in two glasses of warm water that are the same temperature. Wrap a towel or some woollen cloth around one glass and observe the temperature of each glass. The water insulated by the towel or wool will remain warm longer. If you have only one thermometer, then record the findings about one glass first and then the other.

of mineral wool, an insulating material made from the slag (mineral refuse) recovered from iron-making blast furnaces.

Blanket insulation is similar to batt insulation, but it comes in long rolls instead of pieces. A roll usually contains about 100 sq. ft. [9 sq. m] of insulation. Loose-fill insulation comes in bulk form, in bags, or in bales. Mineral wool in the form of pellets, shredded paper, expanded mica, granulated cork, and other materials are types of loose-fill insulation. Loose-fill insulation is poured or blown into place.

Rigid insulation consists of thick sheets of fiberboard. It is usually nailed to the outside walls and

WALL CAVITY INSULATION
The walls of many modern houses are built of two "skins" of masonry, such as brick, with an empty space between them. This cavity can be filled with a foam that hardens and acts as heat and sound insulation.

clothing provide greater protection than one thick layer with the same total weight. This is due to the insulating effect of the air between the layers. The same principle is applied to insulation in homes and other structures. For example, the layer of air between storm windows and the regular windows provides insulation.

Home insulation is extremely important for comfortable and economical living. The loss of heat in uninsulated houses is so high that insulation in the outside walls and top ceilings quickly pays for itself in lower fuel bills. In most modern houses, the hollow spaces in walls and ceilings are usually filled with insulation. Several types of insulation are used for houses: batt insulation, blanket insulation, loose-fill insulation, rigid insulation, and reflective insulation.

Batt insulation is made in soft, flexible units that fit between rafters and joists. Batts are made of fireproof, fibrous material, such as treated wood fiber, flax fiber, eel grass, or shredded paper. This material is stitched between two layers of waterproof paper. Batts are available in thicknesses up to 6 in. [15 cm]. The fill material in batts may also be made

These black insulators are made from a glasslike material. They are used to support high-voltage power lines because they do not allow electricity to flow through them.

then covered with wood siding or bricks. Reflective insulation consists of thin copper or aluminum sheets, or of copper or aluminum foil. It is often applied to the surfaces of rigid insulation, plaster-board, or even heavy paper. The metallic surfaces of these materials reflect heat.

Other kinds of heat and cold insulation include asbestos and cork. Both materials have specialized uses. Asbestos is sometimes used to insulate fur-naces and hot pipes. Cork is used in refrigeration. Asbestos has been shown to cause cancer and lung disease. Therefore, the use of asbestos is now closely regulated in many countries (see ASBESTOS).

Refractory materials are used to insulate against high temperatures in industrial furnaces, boilers, and incinerators. Refractories are made of non-metallic substances such as quartzite, sandstone, fire clay, bauxite, and graphite. They withstand temperatures of up to 3,632°F [2,000°C], well over the melting point of iron. Refractories also resist thermal shock (sudden large changes in tempera-ture) and chemical actions of gases and liquids.

Soundproofing is a type of insulation. There are two different types. One type consists of sound-absorbing or sound-deadening materials placed on walls and ceilings. These materials make a speaker's voice more audible and reduce echoes. Materials used for this purpose include perforated cardboard, fiber-board, corkboard, and special types of acoustical tiles and plaster. These materials contain many air pas-sages that take excess energy away from sound waves.

Another type of soundproofing reduces the sound transferred from room to room by vibration of the walls and floors. Sound waves make these surfaces vibrate. This causes air in contact with these surfaces to vibrate and cause other sounds. This type of sound transmission is difficult to over-come. However, building materials such as con-crete, brick, and stone are used because they produce less vibration than wood and fiberboard. Floor coverings, such as carpets, help insulate against floor vibrations (see ACOUSTICS).

Electrical insulation is made from materials that do not conduct electricity. These materials include rubber, glass, cotton, paraffin, and certain plastics.

PROJECT 13, 31, 56

INSULIN Insulin is a hormone formed in the body by the islets of Langerhans, which are part of the pancreas. The pancreas is an organ located near the stomach (see HORMONE; PANCREAS). Like other hormones, insulin is used to regulate other organs and systems of the body. Insulin acts to help the body use sugar and starches. Insulin gets it name from *insula,* the Latin word for "island."

After a person eats, sugar and starches are converted into a simple sugar called glucose. Glucose is then released in the bloodstream. Insulin is also released into the bloodstream to help the body use the glucose for energy. Insulin also helps the body use amino acids, the chemicals that form proteins.

Insulin is the "spark" that helps the body convert glucose into energy. In healthy people, the body produces enough insulin to utilize glucose from their food. If a person does not produce enough insulin, the body cannot use or store glucose, and the sugar builds up in the bloodstream. This condition is called diabetes mellitus. A person who has the condition is called a diabetic.

Before 1921, a person who had diabetes usually did not live very long. In 1921, two Canadians, physician Frederick Banting and medical student Charles Best, were able to isolate the insulin-producing cells from the pancreas of animals. They were awarded the Nobel Prize for medicine and physiology in 1923 for their work (see BANTING, SIR FREDERICK GRANT).

Insulin taken from the glands of pigs and cows butchered for food is used to keep alive millions of people who suffer from diabetes. The insulin from pigs and cows differs slightly from human insulin, and some people are allergic to some of the other protein molecules found in the insulin. Recent research has resulted in production of human insulin by changing the pig insulin molecule. Also, the human gene that controls the production of insulin has been put into bacteria, which then produce human insulin. Many diabetics are now taking such human insulin.

Because it is a protein, insulin usually cannot be taken orally. It would be digested and thus destroyed. Therefore, insulin must be injected into the body (see INJECTION).

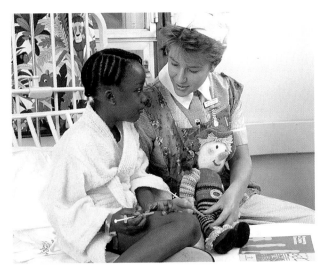

INSULIN

Many people with diabetes need to have regular injections of insulin. Here a nurse shows a girl how to inject herself by demonstrating on a doll.

There are two main forms of diabetes mellitus: insulin-dependent diabetes mellitus (Type I) and noninsulin-dependent diabetes mellitus (Type II). People with insulin-dependent diabetes do not produce enough insulin. Such diabetics must give themselves insulin injections, timed with meals and exercise, to help keep the blood sugar at normal levels. People with noninsulin-dependent diabetes cannot produce enough insulin to cope with the large increase in blood glucose levels. Most people with this type of diabetes can control the disease through a careful diet.

New treatments for diabetes have recently been developed. Some diabetic patients can be cured with a pancreas transplant. In transplant surgery, the healthy pancreas of a person who has died replaces the diseased pancreas of the diabetic (see TRANSPLANTATION). An artificial pancreas, which is like a small pump implanted in the patient's body, can also be used to treat diabetes. By automatically releasing insulin throughout the day, the artificial pancreas eliminates the need for insulin injections. *See also* DIABETES.

INTEGRATED CIRCUIT An integrated circuit, or IC, consists of various electronic components and their connections, all of which are produced on a small piece, or wafer, of silicon. This wafer is called a chip (see CHIP). Silicon is a semiconducting material that is neither a good conductor nor a nonconductor (see SEMICONDUCTOR). Silicon replaces the wires previously used to connect components in electronic circuits. Different amounts of impurities are added to the silicon to make different parts of the chip act like individual electronic components, such as capacitors, resistors, diodes, and transistors (see CAPACITOR AND CAPACITANCE; DIODE; RESISTANCE; TRANSISTOR).

Integrated circuits have many advantages over individual electronic components. They are much smaller and lighter, and they operate faster. They use much less power, cost less, and last longer. ICs also make repairing electronic devices easier, since the entire chip is simply replaced instead of having to find individual faulty parts.

The first integrated circuits were built in the 1960s. They were used in military equipment and spacecraft and helped make possible the first manned space flights. ICs were later used in radios, television sets, computers, and other electronic devices. Development of complex ICs called microprocessors led to their widespread use in producing smaller, more economical electronic devices in the early 1970s. These devices include pocket-sized calculators, digital watches, video games, and controls to operate some types of home appliances and industrial machines. Microprocessor technology also led to the development of microcomputers. Computers can now be made small enough to be held in a hand.

See also COMPUTER; MICROCHIP; MICROELECTRONICS.

INTELLIGENCE Most scientists define intelligence as the ability to learn, understand, remember, or solve problems. People differ in the speed at which they learn things. They differ in their ability to understand ideas. They differ in how well and how long they remember ideas. They also differ in how they use their knowledge and memory of situations in the past to solve problems. There is no fully accepted definition of intelligence. However, intelligence involves all of the abilities mentioned above.

Many psychologists (scientists who study behavior) believe that intelligence can be measured with various kinds of tests. The intelligence tests serve as an indication of how well a person may do when facing specific problems in everyday life. Psychologists figure the results of an intelligence test and assign it a number called an IQ. *IQ* stands for "intelligence quotient." To determine an IQ, tests are given to find a person's mental age. The mental age is found by comparing test results with what is expected of people the same age.

An 8-year-old and a 16-year-old may both have the mental age of 12. The mental age of the younger child is far above his or her chronological age (age in years). The 16-year-old's mental age is far below his or her chronological age. Psychologists have developed a formula for comparison purposes:

$$IQ = \frac{MA \text{ (mental age)}}{CA \text{ (chronological age)}} \times 100$$

First, the mental age is divided by the chronological age. When the quotient is multiplied by 100, the resulting number is the IQ. This number is used to show how someone's intelligence compares with that of other people of the same chronological age. In the example above, the 8-year-old child's IQ is 150—above the average, which is 100. The 16-year-old's is 75—which is below average.

Many people believe that intelligence tests do not really measure intelligence. They think that many intelligence tests measure only what someone has learned rather than actual abilities to think and reason. These people point out that the tests do not measure how quickly or slowly a person learns, which is an important component of intelligence. Therefore, they say that most intelligence tests do not give a complete picture of the many factors that make up intelligence.

Scientists do studies to learn about the factors that affect intelligence. People's intelligence depends both on their heredity and their environment. Every person is born with a certain mental ability, which is inherited. However, environmental factors, such as diet and upbringing, can affect the development of intelligence.

See also BINET, ALFRED.

INTENSITY Intensity is the measure of the strength of certain energy, such as light, magnetism, and sound. Light intensity is measured in units called candelas (see CANDELA). The intensity of a magnetic field is measured in units of tesla or gauss. The intensity of the earth's magnetic field is about 5×10^{-5} tesla. Sound intensity is measured in watts per square centimeter (see WATT). When measuring the difference in intensity of two sounds, a unit called the bel is used. Each bel means an increase or decrease of ten times the intensity. Therefore, if a fire engine siren has an intensity ten times greater than the intensity of a buzzer, the siren has an intensity one bel greater than the buzzer. The decibel (one tenth of a bel) is the more common unit for measuring sound intensity.

See also DECIBEL.

INTERFERENCE Interference occurs when two waves combine to reinforce or cancel each other out (see WAVE). The two waves must have about the same wavelength to interfere. The wavelength is the distance between one crest (high point) and the next.

Interference can occur with any kind of wave, such as water waves, sound waves, light waves, and

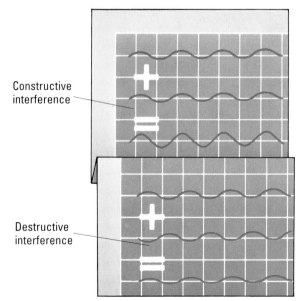

INTERFERENCE

When two waves are in step (in phase), they combine to form a bigger wave. This is called constructive interference. In destructive interference, two waves are out of phase and cancel each other.

radio waves. One way to produce interference is to pass a beam of light through two holes that are side by side—for example, in a piece of paper. This splits light waves up. After light waves pass through the holes, the waves from each hole recombine and interfere. In some places, the crests of the waves coincide. At these points, the light is strongest. This is called constructive interference. In other places, the crest of one wave coincides with the trough of the other. This is called destructive interference. The two waves cancel each other out. The resulting pattern of light is a series of light and dark bands. This is called an interference pattern.

INTERFEROMETER An interferometer is an instrument that produces interference to measure some property of the waves passed through the interferometer (see INTERFERENCE). Albert Michelson, an American physicist, invented a very accurate interferometer around 1880 (see MICHELSON, ALBERT ABRAHAM). In the Michelson interferometer, a beam of light is split by a special mirror, which reflects some of the light and allows the rest to pass through it. The two beams are then recombined by other mirrors. The beams travel different distances and therefore are out of step. Because they are out of step, they interfere destructively. The interference pattern can be viewed. Such interferometers are used to measure the wavelengths of light rays. Interference can also be produced between two radio waves. This effect is used in radio astronomy. Two radio telescopes pick up signals from the same source. These two signals are then combined in an interferometer. Their interference pattern allows scientists to measure the wavelength of the radio waves.

See also RADIO ASTRONOMY; TELESCOPE.

INTERFERON Interferons are a group of substances produced mainly by certain lymphocytes. Lymphocytes are a kind of white blood cell and are part of the immune system of mammals.

Interferons were discovered in 1957 (see BLOOD; IMMUNITY; LEUCOCYTE). Interferons are produced by the lymphocytes called T cells whenever a virus is present in the body (see VIRUS). One kind of interferon stops the virus from reproducing. Another kind of interferon stimulates certain cells called macrophages. Macrophages are the result of a maturing process that the white blood cells called monocytes go through. A macrophage cell consumes pathogens (disease-causing organisms). As it does so, it causes increased production of other immune cells, such as T cells. A third type of interferon creates a condition called viral immunity. This means that while a person is infected with one virus, similar viruses or stronger strains of the same virus that may enter the body are prevented from reproducing.

In 1970, scientists discovered that placing a form of nucleic acid into animals causes their bodies to make interferon (see NUCLEIC ACID). This meant the animals had an improved ability to fight viruses. In the 1980s, scientists were able to make human cells produce interferon by adding certain foreign substances to them. Also, scientists used cloning techniques to produce interferon in a laboratory (see CLONE). Scientists hope someday to use interferon to prevent disease as well as cure it.

INTERNATIONAL DATE LINE The

international date line is a line on a map that is the ending line for measuring time zones. The international date line mostly follows another line called the 180° meridian (see LATITUDE AND LONGITUDE). On one side of the international date line, it is one day. On the other side of the international date line, it is a day later or earlier.

If the international date line followed the 180° meridian for its total length, it would cross land areas. This would cause confusion about the date for people living in these areas. Therefore, the international date line was established to avoid land areas. The eastern tip of Siberia has the same date

INTERNATIONAL DATE LINE

The international date line, where one day changes to the next, generally follows the 180° meridian.

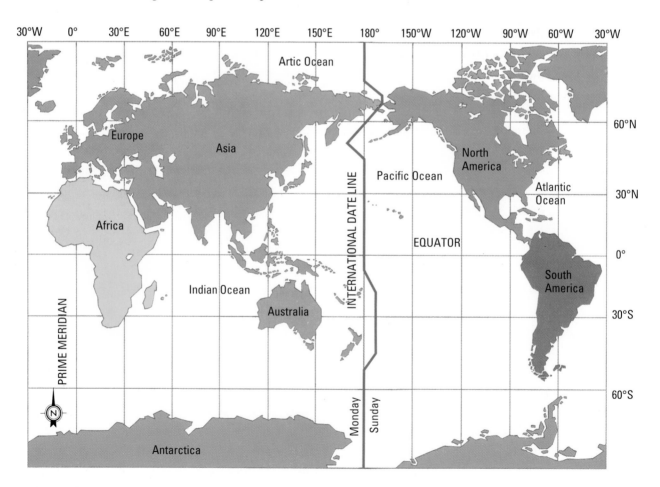

as the rest of Asia. The Aleutian Islands have the same date as the rest of North America. The line also zigzags south of the equator so that New Zealand has the same date as Australia.
See also TIME ZONE.

INTERPOLATION AND EXTRAPOLATION
Interpolation is a way of finding a value at a given point on a graph from already-known values on either side of that point (see GRAPH). For example, if a graph is drawn showing values of x against y, the value of x at any point on the graph can be determined for any value of y by checking against the curve on the graph. This means that the value of x was determined between the known points used to draw the graph—interpolation. If the curve had to be extended beyond the known points to give the value of x, this would be extrapolation.

INTESTINE
The intestine is a long, folded, and looped tube that forms the largest part of the digestive system. It extends from the stomach to the anus. Together with the cavity of the mouth, the esophagus (gullet), and the stomach, it makes up the alimentary canal, or digestive tract (see ALIMENTARY CANAL). The intestine is also called the bowel, or sometimes the gut. Inside it, nearly all the processes of digestion are carried out. All of the food materials that the body absorbs pass through the walls of the intestine into the bloodstream and the lymphatic system (see CIRCULATORY SYSTEM; LYMPHATIC SYSTEM).

In humans, the intestine is divided into two parts, the small intestine and the large intestine. They are given these names because of differences in their widths, not in their lengths. The small intestine is about 1.5 in. [3.75 cm] across at its widest point. The large intestine reaches a width of about 2.5 in. [6.25 cm].

Parts of the intestine
The small intestine starts at the stomach. Its first part is the duodenum. This section receives partly digested food from the stomach. The food enters through a ring of muscle called the pyloric sphincter, which acts as a valve.

Ducts (tubes) from the gallbladder and the pancreas lead into the duodenum (see GALLBLADDER; LIVER; PANCREAS). Digestive juices pass through these ducts.

The duodenum leads into the middle part of the small intestine, which is called the jejunum. The jejunum is connected to the last part of the small intestine, called the ileum, which connects to the large intestine. The first portion of the large intestine is called the cecum. Attached to the cecum is a small close-ended tube called the appendix. It has no known function in humans. However, some rodents, such as rats, have an appendix that helps digestion. Appendicitis is a serious disease that happens if the appendix becomes infected by bacteria (see BACTERIA; DISEASE; INFECTION). The appendix then swells and becomes filled with pus, a yellowish white fluid. Appendicitis is very painful and usually results in surgery to remove the appendix. It is important that appendicitis is treated immediately. Otherwise, the appendix may burst and spread bacteria to other organs in the body.

The cecum leads into the colon, which forms the greater part of the large intestine. The colon extends in a big loop, up the right-hand side of the abdomen, across the front, and down the left-hand side. From there it leads into the part of the large intestine called the rectum, which passes downward through the pelvis. The final part of the large intestine is the anal canal, which opens to the outside at the anus.

The wall of the intestine is made up of several distinct layers. The innermost layer is called the mucosa. It contains cells that secrete mucus and digestive fluids. The middle layer includes sheets of muscle that contract and relax, pushing the food through the intestine. The muscles are covered by a slippery layer of skinlike cells. This slippery coating allows the loops of intestine to move past each other as food moves through the digestive system.

Function of the intestine
The upper part of the small intestine, the duodenum, receives food that the stomach has started to digest. The

duodenum makes its own digestive fluids in the mucosa. It also receives fluids from the pancreas and gallbladder. The digestive fluids and fluid from the pancreas contain enzymes that break down food (see ENZYME).

In the following parts of the small intestine, the jejunum and the ileum, food materials are sent into the bloodstream. Tiny, branching, fingerlike projections, called villi, absorb glucose and amino acids and pass them into the blood. Fatty acids are also absorbed. Fatty acids pass into the lymphatic stream and eventually pass into the bloodstream (see LYMPHATIC SYSTEM). The villi, which make up the inner surface of the small intestine, increase the area through which food material can be absorbed by many hundreds of times.

By the time the contents of the small intestine reach the large intestine, most of the food material has been digested and absorbed. All that remains is undigested food, worn-out cells from the mucosa, dead and dying bacteria, digestive fluids, and water.

In the colon, water and salts are absorbed from the remaining contents and are taken into the bloodstream. By the time the contents reach the end of the colon, they are a semisolid material called feces. The feces are discharged through the anus. From the beginning to the end of the intestine, the contents are pushed along by the muscular intestinal walls (see DIGESTION; STOMACH).

Diseases of the intestine The human intestine may suffer from certain disorders and diseases.

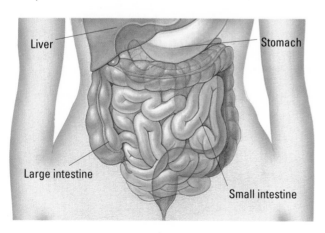

Liver

Stomach

Large intestine

Small intestine

INTESTINE

In an adult human, the small intestine is about 22 ft. [6.6 m] long. The wider large intestine is only about 6 ft. [1.8 m] long.

Some of the more mild conditions may be treated by a change in diet. More serious conditions may require drugs or surgery. Diarrhea is an example of an intestinal disorder. In diarrhea, the intestines frequently pass feces that are loose and watery. Nausea and cramps also may occur. Diarrhea usually results from a viral or bacterial infection in the digestive tract or from food poisoning (see FOOD POISONING; INFECTION; VIRUS). Diarrhea that lasts more than several days should be treated by a doctor. Large amounts of body fluids and salts are lost during diarrhea. They can be replaced by drinking plenty of water and other fluids as directed by a doctor.

Constipation is a disorder in which feces are passed infrequently. When feces are passed, they are often hard. This makes passing them difficult. Constipation may result from a diet low in fiber, overuse of laxatives, and weakened rectal muscles (see FIBER; LAXATIVE). Rectal muscles may be weakened by certain illnesses and overuse of laxatives. As the feces remain in the intestine, toxins (poisons) may be released into the lymphatic stream and then into the blood. These toxins may cause backaches, headaches, or other symptoms. Constipation that lasts more than several days should be treated by a doctor.

Colitis is a disease in which the colon and other parts of the intestine become inflamed (see INFLAMMATION). The symptoms include diarrhea, fever, and bleeding from the anus. Sometimes, the colon becomes scarred or ulcers (sores) develop. If colitis continues for many years, it may lead to colon cancer or surgery to remove part of the colon (see CANCER). Colitis should be treated by a doctor.

Certain steps can be taken to help keep the intestines healthy and functioning properly. For example, doctors advise drinking plenty of water and eating foods that contain large amounts of dietary fiber (see FIBER). Foods high in fiber include raw or lightly cooked vegetables, fruits, and whole grains. Fiber and water help food wastes stay soft and bulky as they pass through the intestine. This helps prevent constipation. Fiber also helps gently "sweep" the lining of the intestine as it passes. This helps prevent wastes from remaining in the intestine too long and later releasing toxins.

An invention is a new product that someone makes. Inventions have given us power over our environment and help us to have better, easier, and happier lives.

An invention is different from a discovery. A discovery happens when something that is already present in nature is seen or learned about for the first time. An invention, on the other hand, is the making of a new product that no one has ever made before. An invention happens when a person puts knowledge and skill together to make use of discoveries. Many inventions can be both helpful and harmful. The automobile, for example, is a convenient means of transportation. However, it has added greatly to air pollution and also can be dangerous.

Before the 1900s, most inventors worked alone. Many of them had little formal schooling. Today, teams of engineers and scientists, who work together in laboratories, come up with most inventions. The following table lists some of the important inventions of the past five hundred years.

Because of these inventions, people have made great strides in industry, transportation, communication, and medicine over the centuries.

The Chinese invented a great many things, such as paper, gunpowder, rockets, and the spinning wheel. Many of these inventions became known in Europe many centuries after they were first invented in China.

Some inventions have changed history. The Industrial Revolution came about because of the invention of spinning machines (for making cloth) and steam engines to power the spinning machines. The computer and the computer chip have revolutionized many modern businesses and industries.

One of the greatest inventors in history was Thomas Alva Edison. Edison came up with more than a thousand inventions, including the electric light, the phonograph, and movies with sound. Edison spent many hours every day of his life working on inventions. He once said that genius is "1 percent inspiration, and 99 percent perspiration."
See also EDISON, THOMAS ALVA.

RECENT INVENTION
Personal computers (PCs) date from the 1970s. The most recent type is the laptop computer. This is a small, portable PC that has become increasingly popular with business people, reporters, and others who work while traveling.

HISTORY OF INVENTIONS

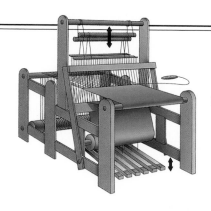

Flying shuttle 1733

Movable printing type 1450

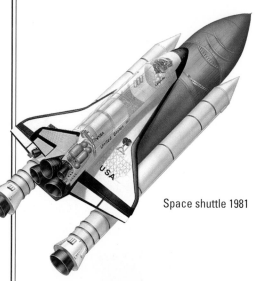

Space shuttle 1981

Electronic pocket calculator 1972

INDUSTRY

1698	Steam pump	Thomas Savery (Britain)
1733	Flying shuttle	John Kay (Britain)
1767	Spinning jenny	James Hargreaves (Britain)
1780s	Double-acting steam engine	James Watt (Britain)
1790s	Cotton gin	Eli Whitney (USA)
1800	Lathe	Henry Maudsley (Britain)
1839	Steam hammer	James Nasmyth (Britain)
1856	Bessemer steel-making process	Henry Bessemer (Britain)
1867	Dynamite	Alfred Nobel (Sweden)
1896	Steam turbine	Charles Curtis (USA)
1930	Cyclotron	Ernest Lawrence (USA)
1960	Laser	Theodore Maiman (USA)
1962	Integrated circuits (silicon)	Jack S. Kilby (USA)
1972	Electronic pocket calculator	Jack S. Kilby, J.D. Marriman, and J.H. Van Tussel (USA)

TRANSPORTATION

1801	Steam locomotive	Richard Trevithick (Britain)
1837	Screw propeller	John Ericsson (Sweden)
1877	Four-stroke internal combustion engine	Nikolas August Otto (Germany)
1885	Gasoline engine	Karl Benz and Gottlieb Daimler (Germany)
1887	Railway telegraph system	Granville T. Woods (USA)
1888	Pneumatic tire	John Dunlop (Britain)
1893	Diesel engine	Rudolf Diesel (Germany)
1903	Powered airplane	Wilber and Orville Wright (USA)
1937	Jet engine	Frank Whittle (Britain)
1969	Jumbo jet	Joe Sutherland (USA)
1981	First space shuttle in space (*Columbia*)	NASA (USA)

COMMUNICATIONS

1450	Movable printing type	Johannes Gutenberg (Germany)
1608	Refracting telescope	Hans Lipershey (Holland)
1811	Mechanical printing press	Friedrich Koenig (Germany)
1830s	Photography	Joseph Niépce and Louis J.M. Daguerre (France), Willam Fox Talbot (Britain)
1837	Telegraph	William Cooke and Charles Wheatstone (Britain), Samuel Morse (USA)
1876	Telephone	Alexander Graham Bell (USA)
1877	Record player	Thomas Alva Edison (USA)

Jumbo jet 1969

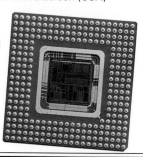

Integrated circuits 1962

Steam
locomotive
1801

Screw propeller 1837

1888	Facsimile telegraphy system	Elisha Gray (USA)
1895	Radio	Guiglielmo Marconi (Italy)
1920s	Television	John Logie Baird (Britain), Vladimir Zworykin (USA)
1939	Digital computer	John Atanasoff (USA)
1948	Transistor	William Shockley, John Bardeen, W.H. Brattain (USA)
1955	Video recorder	Charles P. Ginsberg, Charles E. Anderson, and Ray M. Dolby (USA)
1964	Holography	Emmett Norman Leith, Juris V. Upantnicks, and C.W. Stroke (USA)
1983	Compact disc technology	Joop Sinhou (Netherlands) and Toshi Tada Doi (Japan)
1990	SERODS storage technology	Tuan Vo-Dinh and David Stokes (USA)

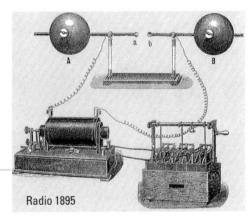

Photography
1830s

MEDICINE

1590	Compound microscope	Zacharias Janssen (Netherlands)
1593	Thermometer	Galileo Galilei (Italy)
1816	Stethoscope	René T.H. Laenec (France)
1867	Antiseptic spray apparatus	Joseph Lister (Britain)
1895	X-ray machine	Wilhelm Roentgen (Germany)
1954	Polio vaccine	Jonas Salk (USA)
1972	Magnetic resonance imaging (MRI)	P.C. Lauterbur (USA)
1978	In vitro fertilization	Robert G. Edwards and Patrick C. Steptoe (Britain)
1985	Laser coronary angioplasty	James Forrester, Warren Grvadiest, and Frank Litvak (USA)

HOUSEHOLD

1845	Sewing machine	Elias Howe (USA)
1852	Safety elevator	Elisha Graves Otis (USA)
1867	Typewriter	Christopher L. Sholes and Carlos Glidden (USA)
1879	Electric light	Thomas Alva Edison (USA)
1947	Microwave oven	Percy LeBaron Spencer (USA)
1957	Velcro	Georges deMestral (Switzerland)
1972	Windsurfer	James Drake and Hoyle Schweitzer (USA)

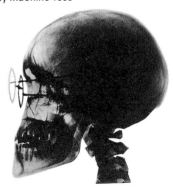

Radio 1895

X-ray machine 1895

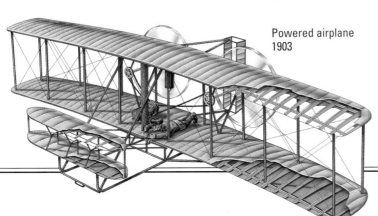

Powered airplane
1903

997

INVERSE SQUARE LAW The inverse square law is a way of calculating how some forces and forms of energy are affected by their distance from their source. If you are standing one foot away from a fire, and move three feet away, you have increased the distance three times. You might think that you would, therefore, receive one-third as much heat. This is not so. The inverse square law says that you receive only one-ninth as much heat. You must take the square of the distance (that is, the distance times itself) to calculate the heat intensity.

Using the inverse square law, scientists calculate how much light will reach different planets. For example, Pluto is 400 times farther away from the sun than is Earth. The square of 400 is 160,000. Therefore, according to the inverse square law, the brightness of the sunlight on Pluto is 1/160,000th of the brightness of sunlight on Earth.

The inverse square law applies to forces and forms of energy that spread out from a source. However, it only applies if the source is small compared to the distance between the source and the observer. Light, heat, X rays, radio waves, sound waves, magnetism, and gravity are all governed by the inverse square law.

INVERSION LAYER An inversion layer is a band of air in the lower part of the atmosphere that has cooler air nearer the ground, not warmer air, as is usual. Normally, warm air rises and is replaced by cooler clean air (see CONVECTION). An inversion layer often develops on cool, clear nights near the earth's surface as the ground cools. The cold layer of air stays near the ground with the warmer air above it. Because the air is cool, convection does not take place. The cooler air is trapped near the surface and cannot rise and carry away dust and pollution. This can cause dense smog over cities. Inversion layers can also form when warm air flows over cold land or sea surfaces.

INVERTEBRATE An invertebrate is an animal without a backbone inside its body. More than 90 percent of all animal species are invertebrates, and they include insects, mollusks, and worms. Some invertebrates are so small that they can be seen only under a microscope. Others are huge, such as the giant squid, which can be over 50 ft. [15 m] long with its tentacles extended.

Many invertebrates have no skeleton at all. They must depend on the pressure of body fluids to give them their shape. Some invertebrates have tough skeletons called exoskeletons on the outside of their bodies.
See also SKELETON; VERTEBRATE.

INVERTEBRATE

The East African uraniid moth (top) is an insect and thus a member of one of the largest classes of invertebrates. The prawns, crab, and lobster (bottom) are types of arthropod, another major invertebrate class.

IODIDE An iodide is a compound of the element iodine with another element (see COMPOUND; ELEMENT; IODINE). The simplest iodide is hydrogen iodide, also called hydriodic acid. It has the formula HI.

With metals, iodine forms salts, which are iodides belonging to the class of compounds called halides (see HALOGEN). Sodium iodide and potassium iodide are two such salts. They are found in seawater and in seaweed. Potassium iodide is added to table salt to help prevent goiter, a swelling of the thyroid gland in the neck.

With nonmetallic elements, iodine forms compounds that are not so stable as metal iodides. With nitrogen, it forms nitrogen triiodide. This compound is so explosive that the least vibration will set it off.

IODINE Iodine is a fairly common nonmetallic element that forms purplish black, shiny crystals (see ELEMENT). The chemical symbol for iodine is I. Iodine is a member of the halogen family of elements. It is not as reactive as the other halogens (see HALOGEN). Iodine is not found free in nature but is always found combined with other elements. It has a valence of one in most of its compounds (see COMPOUND; VALENCE). Iodides are compounds of iodine with one or more other elements. Hydrogen iodide (HI) is also called hydriodic acid. With hydrogen and oxygen, iodine forms iodic acid (HIO_3) (see IODIDE).

Iodine is a strong antiseptic (see ANTISEPTIC). It can be dissolved in alcohol to form tincture of iodine. Compounds of iodine also are used to make dyes and photographic chemicals.

IODINE
Seaweed contains compounds of iodine, which can be extracted and used as a source of the element.

Iodine is important to health. The thyroid gland, in the neck, needs iodine to make thyroid hormones (see HORMONE). Most people get enough iodine in their diet to stay healthy. However, in some areas of the world there is very little iodine in the soil. Food grown in these regions lacks iodine. A person who does not get enough iodine may develop goiter. Goiter is a swelling of the thyroid gland. To help prevent goiter, most table salt is now iodized. This means that a little potassium iodide is added to it.

Iodine has several radioactive isotopes that can be made in a laboratory (see RADIOACTIVITY). The most useful isotope is iodine-131 (I-131), called radio-iodine.

Chemists can test for the presence of iodine by using starch. A solution of starch turns blue when iodine is added to it. In the same way, iodine can be used to test for the presence of starch. If a few drops of tincture of iodine are put on a slice of potato, the iodine quickly becomes blue, showing that it is in contact with starch.

Iodine is found in seawater, seaweed, brine from oil wells, and water from mineral springs. Iodine can be obtained from all of these sources. Iodine was discovered by the French chemist Bernard Courtois in 1811. He isolated it in seaweed. Iodine has the atomic number 53, and its relative atomic mass is 126.9044. When solid iodine is heated, it turns into a vapor at 236°F [113.6°C]. A substance that turns from solid directly into vapor is said to sublime (see SUBLIMATION). When iodine is heated under pressure, it does not sublime. Iodine under pressure turns into a liquid at 236°F [113.6°C]. Pressurized liquid iodine boils, or turns into a vapor, at 361°F [183°C]. Iodine vapor has two atoms in each molecule. Its formula is therefore I_2. The vapor is purple in color and very dense.

IONOSPHERE The ionosphere is an electrically charged zone of the earth's atmosphere (see ATMOSPHERE). It extends from a height of about 50 mi. [80 km] to about 300 mi. [480 km] above the earth. X rays and ultraviolet radiation from the sun cause nitrogen and oxygen molecules in the atmosphere to lose electrons. The result is the formation

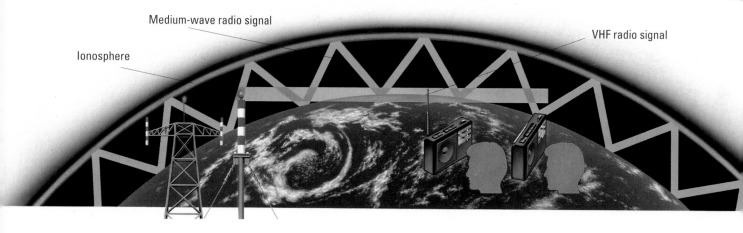

Ionosphere — Medium-wave radio signal — VHF radio signal

IONOSPHERE

The ionosphere is a layer of ionized gas (charged particles) in the upper atmosphere. The ions reflect medium-wave radio signals, which can therefore "bounce" around the world. VHF radio signals, by contrast, travel in straight lines through the lower atmosphere; they do not bounce off the ionosphere.

of a layer of charged particles. The ionosphere reflects some radio waves, allowing them to travel around the world. The ionosphere is not uniform throughout. The lower layer of the ionosphere is called the Heaviside-Kennelly layer, or E layer. It reflects medium radio waves. Higher up, the Appleton layer, or F layer, reflects short radio waves.

IONS AND IONIZATION
An ion is an atom or group of atoms that has lost or gained electrons (see ATOM). As a rule, an atom has an equal number of electrons and protons. The number is the same as the atomic number. Electrons each have one negative electric charge. Protons each have one positive electric charge. The numbers of negative and positive charges are the same, so the atom is electrically neutral. However, the electrons that orbit the nucleus are not bound to the nucleus as the protons are and can escape from the atom. When an electron escapes, it leaves an "extra" proton in the nucleus. The atom is left with a positive electric charge. It has become a positive ion.

Hydrogen is the simplest element (see ELEMENT). Each atom of hydrogen has just one proton in its nucleus and one electron. It can lose only one electron, so a hydrogen ion has just one positive charge. Larger atoms may lose one, two, three, or even four electrons. There are few ions with more than four charges. In cases when electrons are added to an atom, they increase the number of negative charges. Then, negative ions are formed.

To show how many charges an ion has, chemists use plus and minus signs. A hydrogen ion is written H^+. This shows that it has one positive charge.

COMMON IONS

Valence 1	Valence 2	Valence 3
Ammonium NH_4^+	Barium Ba^{2+}	Aluminum Al^{3+}
Bicarbonate HCO_3^-	Carbonate CO_3^{2-}	Chromic Cr^{3+}
Chlorate ClO_3^-	Cupric Cu^{2+}	Ferric Fe^{3+}
Chloride Cl^-	Ferrous Fe^{2+}	Phosphate PO_4^{3-}
Cuprous Cu^+	Mercuric Hg^{2+}	
Hydoxide OH^-	Plumbous Pb^{2+}	
Mercurous Hg^+	Sulfate SO_4^{2-}	
Nitrate NO_3^-	Sulfite SO_3^{2-}	
Sodium Na^+	Zinc Zn^{2+}	

IONS AND IONIZATION—Electric charges

Ions carry one or more electric charges. The valence of an ion equals the number of charges—positive or negative. For example, the chloride ion (Cl^-), with one negative charge, has a valence of 1. The ammonium ion (NH_4^+) also has a valence of 1. Ions with a valence of 2 include carbonate (CO_3^{2-}) and sulfate (SO_4^{2-}). Aluminum (Al^{3+}) and phosphate (PO_4^{3-}) are ions with a valence of 3.

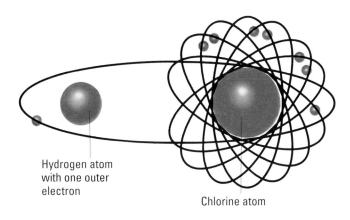

Hydrogen atom
with one outer
electron

Chlorine atom

Hydrogen ion

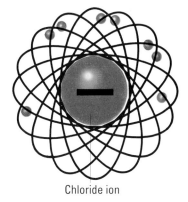

Chloride ion

IONS AND IONIZATION—Ionic bonding

A molecule of hydrogen chloride is pictured above left. Only the outermost electrons of the chlorine atom are shown. When hydrogen chloride is dissolved in water, its molecule separates into two ions, forming an ionic bond (right). The hydrogen atom loses its electron, becoming a positively charged hydrogen ion. The chlorine atom gains this electron, becoming a negatively charged chloride ion.

When a chlorine atom forms an ion, it usually gains one electron. The resulting ion is called a chloride ion and is written Cl^-.

Zinc can form ions with two positive charges. This zinc ion is therefore Zn^{2+}. Sulfate ions have two negative charges: SO_4^{2-}. Aluminum ions (Al^{3+}) and phosphate ions (PO_4^{3-}) each have three electric charges. The number of charges that an ion has is equal to its valence (see VALENCE). Hydrogen can only have a valence of one. However, most elements have more than one valence. Manganese has six different valences. They are different in the different compounds it forms (see COMPOUND).

When an element has more than one valence, different names may be used to tell them apart. Copper forms ions with a valence of one. These are called cuprous ions. Copper also forms ions with a valence of two. These are called cupric ions. In the same way, iron forms ferrous ions (valence two) and ferric ions (valence three). Another way of indicating valences is to use Roman numerals. Ferrous ions can be written as iron (II) and ferric ions written as iron (III).

Ions that have opposite electric charges attract (move toward) each other. Sodium makes a positive ion (Na^+). Chloride is a negative ion (Cl^-).

Together these ions form common table salt. Such ions often form crystals (see CRYSTAL). Compounds formed from ions are called ionic compounds.

If an ionic compound is melted or dissolved, it will conduct electricity. The dissolved compound is called an electrolyte. An electric current will pass between two electrodes dipped into the electrolyte. The process of passing current through an electrolyte is called electrolysis (see ELECTRODE; ELECTROLYSIS). An electrode with a positive electric charge is an anode. It attracts ions with a negative charge. Ions with negative charges are called anions. An electrode with a negative charge attracts positive ions. The electrode is called a cathode. The ions it attracts are called cations. In a solution of sodium chloride, the sodium ions are the cations and the chloride ions are the anions. It is the anions and cations moving through the liquid that carry the electric current.

Ionization is the formation of ions. Ionization occurs when the ions that make up an ionic compound split up. It also happens when electrons are added to or removed from single atoms of any substance. When a gas is heated to a high temperature, it becomes ionized. The glowing gases that make up the sun and stars are all ionized. A gas heated until all of its atoms are ionized is called a plasma (see PLASMA (PHYSICS)).

Other kinds of energy may cause ionization. Radiation such as X rays, gamma rays, and cosmic rays ionizes gases. A beam of electrons will also cause ionization in a gas. Flashes of lightning are caused by electrical energy jumping from atom to atom in ionized gases in the atmosphere.

Beams of ions can be directed by magnetic fields. This is done in particle accelerators and in mass spectrometers (see ACCELERATORS, PARTICLE; SPECTROMETER).

IRIDIUM (ĭ rĭd′ ē əm) Iridium is a rare metallic element much like the metals platinum and osmium. In nature, iridium is usually found mixed with those metals as compounds (see COMPOUND). The chemical symbol for iridium is Ir (see ELEMENT).

Iridium is a very heavy metal. It is used, with platinum, to make bearings for machinery and electrical contacts. On Earth, iridium is a relatively rare element. However, this element is more common in rocks from meteors and asteroids (see ASTEROID; METEOR). The discovery of a thin layer of iridium in Earth rocks that date from the extinction of the dinosaurs (about 65 million years ago) has led some scientists to propose a theory that the dinosaurs became extinct due to a large meteorite or asteroid crashing into the earth (see DINOSAUR).

Iridium has the atomic number 77, and its relative atomic mass is 192.2. Iridium was discovered in 1803 by Smithson Tennant, a British chemist.

IRIS FAMILY The iris family includes about a thousand kinds of perennial flowering plants. Irises are monocotyledons (see MONOCOTYLEDON; PERENNIAL PLANT). Irises grow in temperate, warm, and hot climates throughout the world. Irises usually have intricate, colorful flowers. The leaves of irises are shaped like the blade of a sword and grow from bulbs or corms or from underground stems called rhizomes (see RHIZOME). The rhizomes of iris plants are poisonous.

There are about three hundred species in the genus *Iris*. Most of these grow in warm northern areas. The flowers consist of three sets of three petals. The lower set, called falls, curves out and bends down. The upper set, called standards, curves upward into a dome. The third set, called stylebranches, are really the petallike styles. They cover the reproductive parts of the flower. Insects have to push between them and the full petals to reach the nectar. In many species, the falls have a hairy part called a beard. The flowers exhibit a wide range of colors, and many cultivated hybrids are grown in gardens. The name *iris* comes from the Greek word for "rainbow." The iris is sometimes called the fleur-de-lis, or "lily flower."

IRIS FAMILY

Irises have various common names such as "flag," "lily flower," and fleur-de-lis. Whatever they are called, they are valued for their intricate, colorful flowers.

Iron is a common metallic element that, in its pure form, is silvery gray and shiny. The chemical symbol for iron is Fe. This comes from the Latin word for iron, *ferrum* (see ELEMENT).

Iron is found in many places. The center of the earth is thought to be made of a mixture of iron and nickel. Compounds of iron are mined from the ground as ores (see COMPOUND; ORE). Important ores containing iron are hematite and magnetite (iron oxides), siderite (iron carbonate), and iron pyrites (iron sulfide). Long ago, humans found that iron could be taken from its ores by heating them. Today, people use powerful furnaces to heat the

MAKING IRON AND STEEL

Iron is made from iron ore by heating it with coke and limestone in a blast furnace. Steel is made by blowing oxygen gas into a molten mixture of pig iron and steel scrap. Steel can be rolled, cast, or forged to shape it for a wide variety of uses.

lumps of ore. This process is called smelting. The furnaces are called blast furnaces (see BLAST FURNACE; SMELTING).

When iron ore is smelted, it is mixed with coke, made from coal, and limestone, a rock. During the smelting process, most of the noniron parts of the ore burn away, leaving the iron. This iron, called pig iron, is almost pure. Other elements are then usually mixed with the iron, including carbon, silicon, manganese, phosphorus, and sulfur. Such mixtures form cast iron. Cast iron is very hard and brittle. It is used to make stoves, pipes, radiators, and machine parts (see CAST IRON).

Cast iron is made less brittle by further heating. This gets rid of some of the carbon, which makes cast iron brittle. When the iron contains 3 percent carbon and 1 percent silicon, it is more malleable.

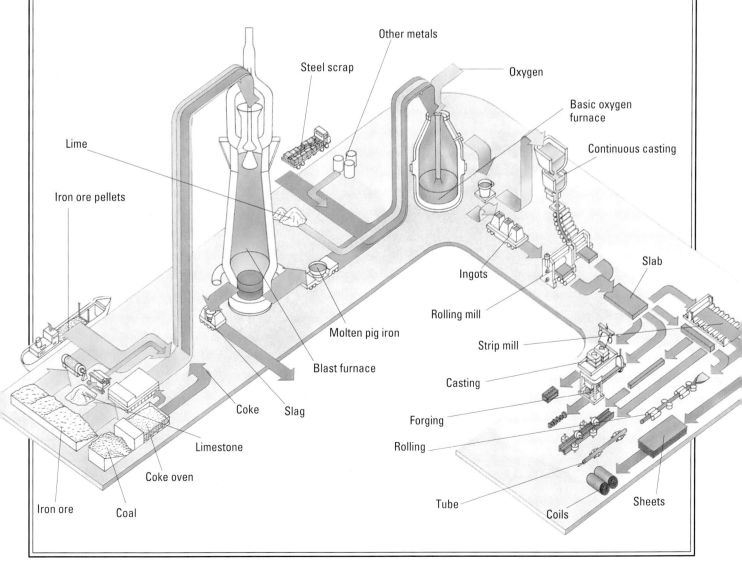

This means that it can more easily be beaten and worked into different shapes. Then the iron can be used to make machinery and tools.

Iron can be made extremely pure by means of a puddling furnace. This has a special lining. The furnace reaches a very high temperature. Most of the impurities are burnt away. The iron that is produced is called wrought iron. Wrought iron is malleable. It is used to make chains, anchors, water pipes, and many other things. The purest iron is made by electrolysis (see ELECTROLYSIS; WROUGHT IRON).

Steel is iron with a little carbon and other elements mixed in. There are many kinds of steel. Low-carbon steel contains only 0.05 percent carbon. High-carbon steel contains up to 1.5 percent carbon. Stainless steel contains about 12 percent chromium. The chromium prevents the steel from rusting. Other steels are made with manganese, nickel, and tungsten (see STEEL).

Iron forms two series of compounds. In ferrous compounds, it has a valence of two. In ferric compounds, it has a valence of three (see VALENCE). Ferrous salts are often pale green, and ferric salts are brown. The rust that forms on iron is mainly ferric oxide (see RUST; SALTS). Iron compounds are used to make pigments (types of dyes) and inks.

Iron is an essential element in the human body. Our red blood cells contain hemoglobin, a red substance that contains iron. Hemoglobin carries oxygen in the blood. Most people get enough iron from the foods they eat. Lack of iron can lead to the disease anemia. People with anemia may be given iron compounds in pills or in injections (see ANEMIA).

Iron is strongly magnetic. Materials that are as magnetic as iron are said to be ferromagnetic. The magnetism of iron is useful in the making of all kinds of electrical machinery. Magnetic iron oxide is used to make tapes for tape and video casette recorders (see MAGNETISM).

Iron has the atomic number 26, and its relative atomic mass is 55.847. This element melts at 2,795°F [1,535°C] and boils at about 5,437°F [3,000°C].

BLAST FURNACE
A blast furnace is kept running day and night. New ingredients are added at the top, while molten iron is run off at the bottom.

IRON AGE The Iron Age was the time in history when people used iron for weapons and tools. It began between 1500 and 1000 B.C. in the Near East and southeastern Europe. The use of iron did not spread to northern Europe until Roman times.

The Iron Age is thought of as the third of the three great ages, after the Stone Age and the Bronze Age. The Iron Age began when people learned how to work iron into hard, durable tools. They used iron for coins, weapons, and farm implements. The increase in trade and communication, in part due to the use of iron, was important to the growth of civilization. *See also* IRON.

IRRADIATION Irradiation is the process of exposing things to radiation. The radiation may be of two basic forms: corpuscular radiation or electromagnetic radiation. Corpuscular radiation is a stream of high-speed nuclear particles, such as neutrons, protons, electrons, or alpha particles. Electromagnetic radiation is in the form of rays, such as gamma rays, ultraviolet rays, or X rays (see ELECTROMAGNETIC RADIATION; RADIATION).

Controlled amounts of radiation are often helpful. For example, carefully controlled radiation can kill cancerous tissue. The gamma radiation given off by the radioactive isotope cobalt-60 is commonly used for this purpose. Treatment of disease by means of radiation is called radiation therapy (see RADIATION THERAPY).

Uncontrolled amounts of radiation can be harmful not only to human beings, but to any living thing. Scientists have found that certain foods can be preserved for months by treating them with X rays or gamma rays to kill decay-producing bacteria (see GAMMA RAY; X RAY). In grain storage elevators, insect pests are sometimes killed by irradiation. Sometimes irradiation is used in insect control to sterilize the males. When this is done, the insects can no longer reproduce (see BIOLOGICAL CONTROL).

Radiation produces mutations in the genes that carry traits from one generation to the next. Mutations are usually harmful. However, irradiation methods have been used to produce helpful mutations in certain plants. For example, the process has been used on rice and wheat to produce hardier, higher-yielding, or earlier-ripening strains. *See also* FOOD PROCESSING; GENETICS; MUTATION.

IRREVERSIBLE REACTION An irreversible reaction is a chemical reaction in which the products—the substances formed by the reaction—cannot be made to reform the reactants—the substances that react together (see CHEMICAL REACTION; COMPOUND; ELEMENT). Many chemical reactions, such as the chemical changes produced by combustion, are irreversible (see COMBUSTION). For example, when wood burns, or combusts, the products of combustion are oxides of carbon and water (which appears as steam). There is no simple way to make wood from these products—combustion is an irreversible reaction. In many other chemical reactions, such as the manufacture of ammonia from nitrogen and hydrogen, it is possible to get back the reactants from the products. Such a reaction is called reversible (see REVERSIBLE REACTION).

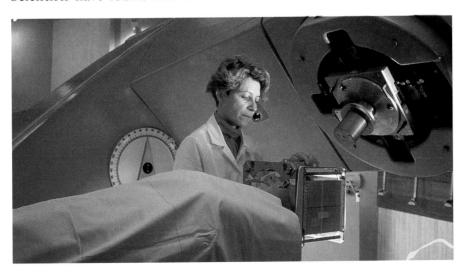

IRRADIATION
A cancer patient has her head held carefully in position while being treated with radiation from a linear accelerator.

IRRIGATION

Irrigation is the watering of land to make it better for farming. Irrigation is usually done in places that do not receive enough rainfall to grow crops.

Humans have irrigated land for thousands of years. The ancient Egyptians used water from the Nile River for irrigation. The ancient Chinese also had elaborate irrigation systems for flooding their rice fields. The ancient Romans built aqueducts to carry water where it was needed (see AQUEDUCT).

Land is irrigated in many different ways. A natural spring may provide enough water for a small farm. In some places, the land is irrigated by groundwater that is pumped to the surface (see GROUNDWATER). Lakes called reservoirs are made by building dams to hold back river water that would otherwise flow to the sea. For example, the Aswan High Dam on the Nile River in Egypt provides water for great stretches of dry land.

Farmers in the United States use several kinds of irrigation systems. They include furrow, flood, spray or sprinkler, and trickle irrigation. Furrow irrigation involves digging narrow ditches between rows of crops. Water flows out of a pipe and into the furrows. In flood irrigation, the entire surface of a field is covered with water. Spray irrigation involves applying a mist of water from pipes that lie on the ground or are attached to a device above the ground. In trickle irrigation, water is trickled, or dripped, from plastic tubes directly over the roots of the plants.

Irrigation plays an important part in conservation. When not enough rain falls, farmers cannot grow crops. The soil becomes dry, and wind blows it away. Irrigation can stop this, and crops can be grown with little or no rain.

Irrigation may someday help make it possible for everyone throughout the world to have enough to eat. Irrigation has helped turn much land that was not suitable for farming into fertile farmland. For example, since 1980, India has expanded its irrigated land by 50 percent, to over 109 million acres [44 million hectares]. As a result, its grain production has expanded by nearly 300 percent. Countries with large areas of

irrigated land include Afghanistan, China, Egypt, Italy, India, Iraq, Japan, Mexico, Pakistan, Russia, and the United States.

Irrigation systems must be carefully designed and managed to avoid environmental problems. Too much irrigation and lack of proper drainage can cause land to become waterlogged. The excess water may run off, causing erosion (see EROSION). Another problem results when salty water is used for irrigation. The salt in the water is not used by the plants and remains in the soil. Over time, the soil may become useless because it is too salty for crops to grow in it. Groundwater used for irrigation may cause another problem. The aquifers in which groundwater is found may dry up. This would reduce or eliminate water available for other uses, such as for household and industrial use. Draining aquifers may also cause the land to sink. For example, the San Joaquin Valley in California sank about 30 ft. [9 m] in fifty-two years. Since the 1970s, surface water has been used for irrigation in the San Joaquin Valley. This has stopped the ground from sinking (see AQUIFER).

Around 5 percent of all farmland in the United States is irrigated, and 13 percent of all United States farms use some form of irrigation. In the

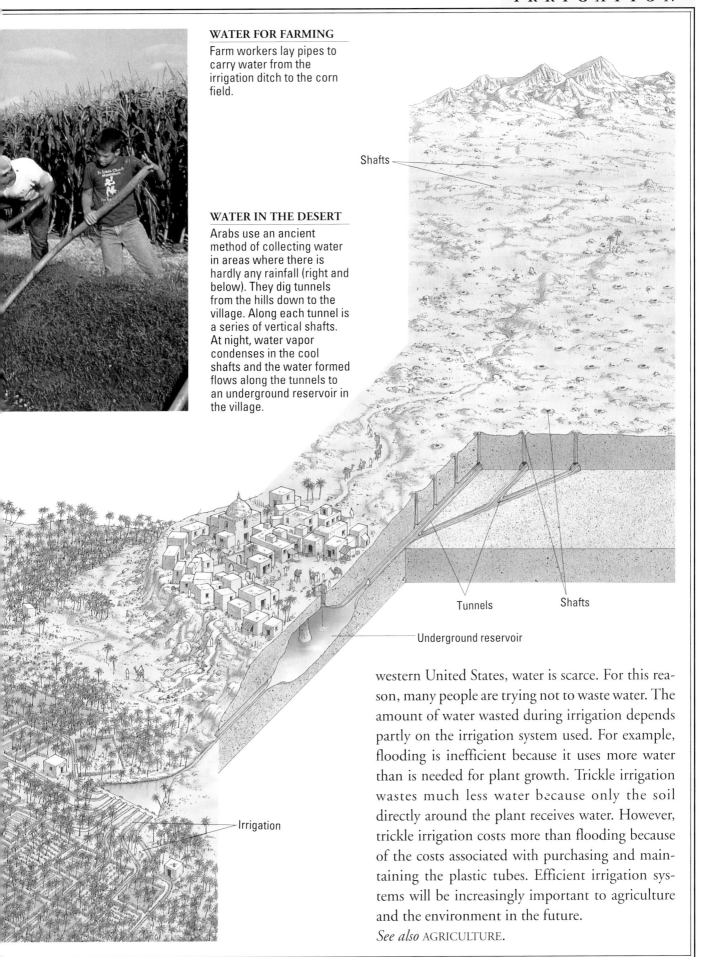

WATER FOR FARMING
Farm workers lay pipes to carry water from the irrigation ditch to the corn field.

WATER IN THE DESERT
Arabs use an ancient method of collecting water in areas where there is hardly any rainfall (right and below). They dig tunnels from the hills down to the village. Along each tunnel is a series of vertical shafts. At night, water vapor condenses in the cool shafts and the water formed flows along the tunnels to an underground reservoir in the village.

Shafts

Tunnels

Shafts

Underground reservoir

Irrigation

western United States, water is scarce. For this reason, many people are trying not to waste water. The amount of water wasted during irrigation depends partly on the irrigation system used. For example, flooding is inefficient because it uses more water than is needed for plant growth. Trickle irrigation wastes much less water because only the soil directly around the plant receives water. However, trickle irrigation costs more than flooding because of the costs associated with purchasing and maintaining the plastic tubes. Efficient irrigation systems will be increasingly important to agriculture and the environment in the future.

See also AGRICULTURE.

ISOBAR AND ISOTHERM Isobars are lines on a weather map that connect places of equal barometric pressure. Barometric pressure is the pressure of air upon the earth's surface (see AIR). Isotherms are lines on a weather map that connect places with equal temperature.

Isobars are an important aid to weather forecasting. Meteorologists (persons who study and forecast weather) can use isobars to predict storm movements and wind direction. Isotherms are also important for forecasting weather. Meteorologists can use isotherms to locate fronts, along which storms often lie, as well as to forecast temperatures. *See also* FRONT; METEOROLOGY; WEATHER.

ISOMER Isomers are substances that have identical chemical compositions but different arrangements of atoms in their molecules (see ATOM; MOLECULE). For example, two different isomers can be made from the following: two carbon atoms, six hydrogen atoms, and one oxygen atom. One way of arranging the atoms is in this shape:

This makes a molecule of ethyl alcohol, or ethanol. Another way of arranging them would be:

This makes a molecule of dimethyl ether. These two substances, ethanol and dimethyl ether, are isomers.

Isomers are very common in organic compounds (see COMPOUND). Organic compounds contain carbon atoms, often linked together in chains. The chains may be straight or branched. There are many ways of arranging the same atoms. The more carbon atoms there are, the more possible isomers there are.

There are several different kinds of isomers. Structural isomers have simple differences in shape. Butane and isobutane are structural isomers. They both have the formula C_4H_{10}. Butane has its four carbon atoms in a straight line. In isobutane, the carbon atoms are arranged in a T-shape:

Butane

Isobutane

Stereoisomers have groups of atoms in different places in their molecules. Maleic and fumaric acids are stereoisomers. They both have two –COOH groups of atoms. In fumaric acid, the groups are on

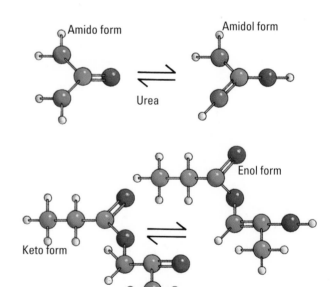

ISOMER—Tautomerism

Tautomerism is a type of isomerism in which a substance exists as two isomers at the same time, sometimes switching between one form and the other.

ISOMER—Stereoisomers

Two types of stereoisomerism are shown here. Ethyl alcohol and dimethyl ether are isomers with the same atoms, but they are joined to different partners in each molecule. In the cis and trans forms of dichloroethylene, atoms have different positions in relation to the carbon-carbon double bond.

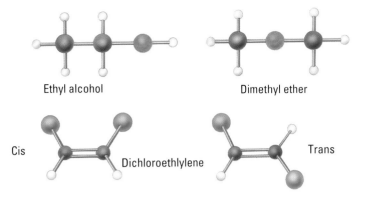

Ethyl alcohol

Dimethyl ether

Cis

Dichloroethlylene

Trans

opposite sides of the molecule. The isomer is called the trans form. In maleic acid, the groups are on the same side. The isomer is called the cis form. This kind of isomerism is called cis-trans isomerism, or geometric isomerism.

Optical isomers have molecules that are mirror images of each other. They differ in the way a left-hand glove differs from a right-hand glove. Thus, optical isomers are called d- or dextro (right-handed) and 1- or laevo (left-handed) forms.

Tautomerism is another kind of isomerism. Tautomers may be changed into one another by a movement of atoms in the molecule. Tautomers exist together in equilibrium. If one of the forms is taken away from a mixture, some of the other forms will change to replace it. The balance of the mixture will be restored.

ISOSTASY (ī sŏs′ tə sē) Isostasy is the equilibrium, or state of balance, of the earth's crust. C.E. Dutton developed the theory of isostasy in 1889. According to the theory, the rocks of the earth's crust "float" on the plastic (nonrigid) rocks of the earth's mantle. Where these crustal rocks are thickest and least dense, they float highest and form continents. The thinner, denser crustal rocks float lower, forming the ocean floors. Movements of the earth's crust are thought to keep the isostatic balance. It is also thought that mountains have "roots" below the surface that balance their mass above the surface (see EARTH). Isostatic balance can be disturbed. For example, the melting of a large area of ice reduces the mass above the surface. The land must rise to keep isostasy.

The land in the arctic region is still rising about 39 in. [1 m] every one hundred years as a result of the melting of the ice sheets from the late

Pleistocene epoch. This period ended about ten thousand years ago.

See also GEOLOGICAL TIME SCALE; GLACIATION; MOUNTAIN.

ISOTOPE Isotopes are atoms of the same element that differ in mass because they have different numbers of neutrons in their nuclei (plural of *nucleus*) (see ATOM; ELEMENT). Nearly all elements are mixtures of isotopes. Chlorine, for example, is a mixture of two isotopes. One has a mass number of 35. The other has two extra neutrons and thus has a mass number of 37. The calculated relative atomic mass of an element is based on the abundance of each of the element's isotopes. Because the lighter isotope of chlorine is more abundant than the heavier isotope, the relative atomic mass of chlorine is 35.453.

Isotopes are identified by writing the mass number before or after the chemical symbol. The isotopes of chlorine can be written ^{35}Cl and ^{37}Cl, or Cl-35 and Cl-37. The isotope uranium-235 can be written U-235 or ^{235}U. Several elements, such as gold and fluorine, have only one isotope.

Hydrogen is the only element that has different names for its isotopes. Hydrogen with mass number 1 is called simply hydrogen or, sometimes, protium. The isotope with mass number 2 is called deuterium, or heavy hydrogen. Hydrogen-3 is called tritium. Tritium does not exist naturally. It is an artificial isotope (see HYDROGEN).

Some natural isotopes are radioactive (see RADIOACTIVITY). Radioactive isotopes decay into the isotopes of other elements as they give off radiation. These elements may also be radioactive and decay further. Eventually, an element is produced that is not radioactive.

Uranium-238 is radioactive. It decays through a series of thirteen other radioactive isotopes and ends up as stable lead. This process takes millions of years. Some radioactive isotopes have uses in medicine and other fields. Uranium-238 is the heaviest natural isotope. However, heavier radioactive isotopes can be made artificially. This is done by bombarding atoms of heavy elements with neutrons and other particles. This process is carried out in nuclear reactors and particle accelerators (see ACCELERATORS, PARTICLE; NUCLEAR ENERGY).

In chemical reactions, the isotopes of an element behave identically. This is because the chemical properties do not depend on the number of neutrons in the nucleus of each atom. They depend on the electrons outside the nucleus (see CHEMICAL REACTION). The isotopes of an element can be separated because they have different masses. Atoms can be separated by means of a centrifuge (see CENTRIFUGE). A centrifuge spins the mixture of isotopes at tremendously high speed. The isotopes become separated as the densest or heaviest are forced outwards. Beams of isotopes may also be split into heavy and light atoms by electric and magnetic fields (see MASS SPECTROMETER). Another method for separating isotopes is to allow a gas containing different isotopes to diffuse through porous screens at different rates. This is like sieving the gas.

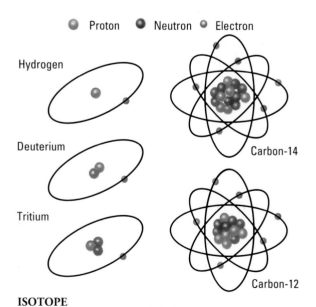

ISOTOPE
The diagram shows the three isotopes of hydrogen, of masses 1, 2, and 3, and two of the isotopes of carbon, of masses 14 and 12.

J

JACARANDA (jăk′ ə răn′də) *Jacaranda* is the name for some kinds of shrubs and trees that grow in warmer parts of North and South America. The wood of the jacaranda is heavy and smells sweet. These trees are popular for planting in warm places. However, they cannot live in colder areas.

The fern-tree jacaranda is a tall, colorful tree often found in the southern United States. It has tiny leaves in bunches that look like fern leaves. In late spring, the fern-tree jacaranda has large bunches of bluish purple flowers.

JACARANDA
The jacaranda tree has fernlike leaves and purple flowers. Though native to the Americas, the jacaranda is also popular in many temperate parts of Australia.

JACKAL The jackal is a wild, doglike animal that lives in Asia, Africa, and some parts of Europe. Because of its sad cry and its yapping, the jackal is sometimes called "the howler." Jackals are mainly scavengers. That is, they feed on animals they find dead. For this reason, they are valued as "street cleaners" in some Asian and African cities. However, jackals also hunt for themselves, eating anything from insects to small antelope. Jackals also eat fruit. The animals have been known to damage bushes and trees on which fruit grows.

The common jackal, or golden jackal, is the commonest of the four species. It looks like a small wolf

JACKAL
Young jackals learn to hunt through play. Shown here are (1) golden jackals; (2) Simien jackals; (3) a sidestriped jackal, and (4) silverbacked jackals.

or coyote. It stands up to about 20 in. [50 cm] at the shoulder. Its length measures from 2 to 3 ft. [61 to 92 cm]. It has a grayish yellow or brown coat and a bushy tail. The other three jackal species, including the silverbacked jackal, live in Africa.

JADE Jade is a hard stone. It is often used to make jewelry and carved ornaments. There are two kinds of jade—one made up of the mineral jadeite, $NaAl(Si_2O_6)$, and the other made up of the mineral nephrite, $Ca_2Mg_5Si_8O_{22}(OH)_2$.

Nephrite is most often the source of jade. Nephrite deposits have been found in New Zealand and North America, especially in Alaska and Wyoming. Nephrite is translucent (allowing some light to pass through) to dark and dull in color. The most valuable kind of nephrite is a dark green jade called spinach jade.

Jadeite is not often found. It is mined mainly in Myanmar (formerly Burma) and China. Jadeite comes in beautiful colors, such as light green and lilac. The best jadeite is quite valuable.

JAGUAR The jaguar is the largest living wild cat in the Western Hemisphere. It lives in Mexico and Central and South America. The jaguar, which has a loud, deep roar, is a skillful hunter. It often lies on tree branches to wait for and leap upon its prey. It feeds on such animals as deer, peccaries, and fish. Using their large paws, jaguars are very good at picking fish out of the water. It also eats young alligators.

A male jaguar may grow to 8 ft. [2.4 m], including its tail, in length. It may weigh up to 300 lb. [136 kg]. Its coat is usually a shade of yellow, having many dark circular markings, usually with a

JADE
Jade is a very hard stone. Here, jadeite has been carved to make a pendant and a pair of earrings.

JAGUAR
The jaguar is the largest cat in the Americas. It resembles the leopard, the equivalent animal in Africa.

spot in the center of each. Some South American jaguars are coal black.

The jaguar population is now endangered. Many forests have been cleared, thus limiting the jaguars' habitat. Also, jaguars are hunted for their valuable fur. The United States does not allow the importing or exporting of jaguar fur.

See also CAT; ENDANGERED SPECIES.

JAMES, WILLIAM (1842–1910) William James was an American psychologist (one who studies how people think and behave). His brother was the writer Henry James. William James studied art, chemistry, medicine, and philosophy. Psychology was not a recognized science at that time. James became interested in psychology while a professor of philosophy at Harvard. He wrote one of the first textbooks on psychology.

James's most famous theory is that chemical changes in the body affect emotions. He worked on this theory with a Danish psychologist named Carl Lange. It is known as the James-Lange theory.

See also EMOTION; PSYCHOLOGY.

JASMINE Jasmines are climbing plants or shrubs of the olive family (see OLIVE FAMILY). There are about 300 species, growing mainly in the warmer

JASMINE
These pale yellow flowers belong to winter jasmine. Common, or summer, jasmine has white flowers.

parts of the Old World. Common jasmine has dark green leaves and bunches of fragrant white flowers. Its blossoms can be used to flavor tea. It also has an oil used in perfumes. Winter jasmine is a popular garden plant because it produces its yellow flowers in the middle of winter.

JASPER Jasper, a mixture of quartz and iron oxide, is a kind of flint. Its formula is SiO_2 (see FLINT). Jasper is often red, but it may also be yellow, white, brown, or black. Sometimes these colors are found in layers in the rock. A hard mineral, jasper can be brightly polished. It is used for mantels, pillars, and other fancy fittings inside buildings. Jasper is found mainly in Greece, India, Poland, Turkey, Russia, and the United States.

JELLYFISH Jellyfish is a name for a kind of sea animal belonging to the phylum Cnidaria (see CNIDARIA). Jellyfish are so called because most of the animal's body looks and feels like jelly. Biologists call the jellyfish a medusa. There are several hundred species, ranging from 0.1 in. to 7 ft. [3 mm to 2.1 m] in diameter.

The body of most jellyfish looks like an umbrella. A short tube in which the mouth is found hangs from the center of the body. Along the edges of this tube are four extensions called oral arms. Jellyfish also have tentacles, which look like strings, hanging from the body. Each kind of jellyfish has its own arrangement of tentacles.

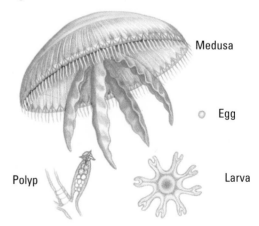

JELLYFISH—Life cycle
A jellyfish begins life as an egg, which develops into a free-swimming larva. The larva changes into a polyp, which attaches itself to the sea bottom. Finally, the jellyfish breaks free and grows into an adult, or medusa.

Jellyfish swim by pushing out the body, like opening an umbrella, then pulling it together quickly. This motion squeezes water out from beneath the body, pushing the jellyfish upward through the water.

Most jellyfish catch small animals with their tentacles or oral arms. These parts have stinging cells that explode when they touch a victim. The food is then passed to the mouth of the jellyfish and swallowed. Some large jellyfish are called sea nettles because of their stinging cells.

Jellyfish produce their young from eggs. These eggs develop into larvae and then into tiny polyps, which rest on the bottom of the sea. Polyps produce jellyfish by budding (see BUDDING). The jellyfish grow on each polyp like a stack of saucers. When the jellyfish reach a certain size, they leave the polyp and grow into adults.

Some jellyfish can give painful and even dangerous stings to people. Small jellyfish called sea wasps carry poison that is deadlier than that of any snake. Sea wasps are found near the coasts of northern Australia and the Philippines.

JENNER, EDWARD (1749–1823) Edward Jenner was an English doctor. He is famous for being the first to use vaccination. Many people caught the disease smallpox in Jenner's time. They were left with scars, and some died of the disease. However, it became known that a person who had had smallpox would not get it again (see IMMUNITY; SMALLPOX). At the same time, there was a cattle disease called cowpox. In western England, people observed that dairymaids who had caught cowpox from their cows did not get smallpox.

In 1796, Jenner took some fluid from a cowpox sore on a dairymaid's finger. He injected this into an eight-year-old boy. The boy never caught smallpox. At first, nobody believed that Jenner's idea worked. However, soon this method of preventing smallpox was being used all over the world.

Jenner's first interest was natural history. He made many discoveries about animals. He observed that a young cuckoo pushes the other little birds out of the nest. He also did studies on the migration of birds.

JET LAG Jet lag is a change of the natural biological clock caused by rapid movement across different time zones (eastwards or westwards) in jet aircraft (see BIOLOGICAL CLOCK). The individual's natural sleep pattern remains in step with the time zone he or she flies from and can take several days to adjust to the local time of the region he or she flies to (see SLEEP). The person may suffer mental and physical exhaustion and disorientation during the period of adjustment, especially if any demanding physical or mental task is attempted.

It is helpful for travelers making long journeys in jet aircraft to try to adjust their sleep pattern to match that of the new time zone before they travel, and to get enough rest once they arrive. Jet lag is not the same as tiredness caused by insufficient sleep during the journey, but lack of sleep will make jet lag worse.

JET PROPULSION

Jet propulsion is the production of motion in one direction by the release of a high-pressure stream of gas in the opposite direction. Jet propulsion is the power that drives jet engines and rockets. Jet engines and rockets burn fuel. This produces large amounts of hot gases very quickly, as in an explosion. The explosion forces the gases out the back through what is called an exhaust nozzle. The gases move at high speed. The engine moves in the other direction from the exhaust gases.

The difference between jets and rockets lies in where the oxygen to burn the fuel comes from. A jet engine uses oxygen in the air around it. It sucks in air to burn its fuel through what is called an intake nozzle. A rocket has no intake nozzle. It carries its own oxygen. The oxygen may be in the form of liquid oxygen in a tank. It may be part of a solid fuel a rocket burns. This is what happens in fireworks rockets.

The jet engines of airplanes have turbine compressors, which are driven by expanding gases produced when compressed air is mixed with fuel and ignited (see COMPRESSOR; TURBINE). The air sucked in through the intake is compressed (squeezed together) before it is mixed with the fuel. This increases the force of the explosion within

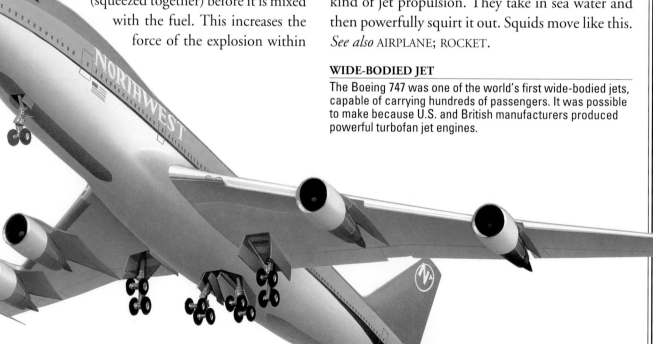

ACTIVITY   *A jet-propelled balloon*

Make a jet-propelled balloon. Take an ordinary balloon and blow it up. Instead of tying the end, hold it pinched between your thumb and forefinger. Then release the balloon. Notice how the air rushing out from the opening pushes the balloon forward. The balloon is moving by means of a kind of jet propulsion.

the engine. A type of engine called a ramjet has no moving parts. The air is "rammed" into the intake by the plane's speed. A ramjet will work only when the plane is moving at high speed. Ramjets are not used for most airplanes.

Many living things in the sea move about by a kind of jet propulsion. They take in sea water and then powerfully squirt it out. Squids move like this. *See also* AIRPLANE; ROCKET.

WIDE-BODIED JET
The Boeing 747 was one of the world's first wide-bodied jets, capable of carrying hundreds of passengers. It was possible to make because U.S. and British manufacturers produced powerful turbofan jet engines.

JET STREAM A jet stream is a band of swift air currents high in the atmosphere. The main part of a jet stream blows at about 6.8 to 8.7 mi. [11 to 14 km] above the earth's surface. Jet streams can be felt strongly at 30,000 ft. [9,000 m] and have been felt as low as 3,000 ft. [915 m] (see ATMOSPHERE).

A jet stream's air currents are shaped like a tube. The center of the jet stream, called the jet core, is the area of highest wind speed. The wind speed ranges from about 65 to 200 mi. [105 to 320 km] per hour.

There is more than one jet stream in the atmosphere. Two of them, the polar jet stream and the subtropical jet stream, have much to do with the weather of the United States. Blowing from west to east, they influence the development of high-pressure (good weather) systems and low-pressure (storm) systems (see WEATHER).

Meteorologists study jet streams by sending special balloons up into the atmosphere. These balloons, called radiosondes, carry special instruments that measure the height, wind speed, and temperature of jet streams (see RADIOSONDE). From this information, meteorologists can predict storm occurrences and movements (see METEOROLOGY).

Pilots during World War II (1939–1945) discovered jet streams. The pilots found that the wind at certain altitudes was strong enough to greatly raise or lower the speed of their planes. Commercial airliners flying eastwards seek out jet streams to help them travel.

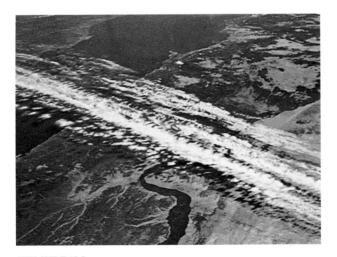

JET STREAM
This bird's-eye view shows a jet stream moving across the Red Sea and the Nile River in the Middle East.

JOINT A joint, in the body, is where a bone meets another bone (see BONE). There are many different kinds of joints in the human body. They can be grouped according to how much one bone is able to move against the other. There are immovable joints, which do not move. There are also partially movable joints, which move a little. Finally, there are freely movable joints, which move in many directions.

In an immovable joint, the bones are held tightly together. The dome of the skull, or cranium, is a box made of bony plates. The plates of bone fit together something like the pieces of a jigsaw puzzle. The plates must be immovable to protect the brain inside. Between the edges of the plates are linking pieces of tough fibrous tissue. The joints where the teeth fit into sockets in the jaw bones are also immovable joints. Immovable joints are also known as fibrous joints.

JOINT—Double-jointed
An acrobat demonstrates the amazing flexibility of his joints. This is because his joints are looser than usual. Such people are called double-jointed.

In a partially movable joint, the bones are linked by cartilage. Cartilage is a very tough, but flexible, material (see CARTILAGE). The joints of the spine are partly movable, so that the spine can bend. Each of the bones in the spine is called a vertebra. Between the vertebrae are disks of cartilage. They are called intervertebral disks. They act as shock absorbers, as well as allowing the vertebrae to move slightly against each other. The joints where the ribs meet the sternum (breastbone) at the front of

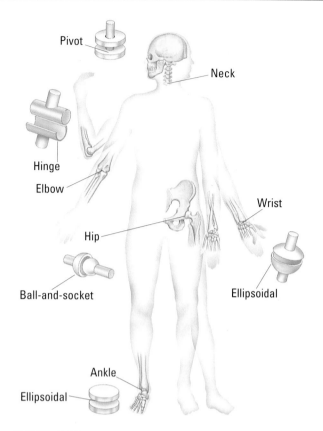

Pivot

Neck

Hinge

Elbow

Wrist

Hip

Ball-and-socket

Ellipsoidal

Ankle

Ellipsoidal

JOINT—Different types

The human body has various kinds of joints, each allowing a different kind of movement. The neck turns using a pivot joint, and hinge joints let the elbows and knees bend. Ball-and-socket joints in the hips permit circular movement. The wrists and ankles turn and bend using ellipsoidal joints.

the chest are also partially movable joints. This kind of joint is also called a cartilaginous joint.

The main joints of the body are the freely movable joints. These are found at the hips and shoulders. They are also found at the elbows and knees and at the wrists and ankles. The ends of the bones that are part of such joints are covered with caps of tough, smooth cartilage. Cartilage does not wear out easily. Its surface is very shiny so that there is very little friction between the moving bones.

In a freely movable joint, the space between the bones is filled with a special fluid called synovial fluid. Synovial fluid acts like oil. It helps the bones and other parts of the joint move easily. The fluid is produced by a thin membrane (layer of tissue) that lines the joint. Synovial fluid is kept within the joint by this synovial membrane. Outside the membrane are tough, flexible ligaments. The ligaments join one bone to the other but allow movement (see LIGAMENT). The membrane and the ligaments together

form what is called the joint capsule. Freely movable joints are also called synovial joints.

Synovial joints are described by their shape or by the movements that they allow. The hip joint allows movement in many directions. This is because the head of the femur (thighbone) is ball shaped. It fits into a cup-shaped socket formed by the bones of the pelvis. The shoulder joint is much like this. This kind of joint is called a ball-and-socket joint. It is the most movable of all joints. At the elbow, the joint is called a hinge joint. It allows the arm to be bent and straightened, but not to bend sideways, as though the two parts of the arm were connected by a hinge. The point at which the skull is joined to the spine is a pivot joint. It allows the head to turn from side to side. Between the small bones inside the hand are gliding joints.

Injuries and diseases may affect joints. Dislocation is when the bones are pulled or knocked out of their position in the joint. Arthritis is a painful disease that attacks cartilage in joints. Most freely movable joints can now be replaced by an artificial joint, or prosthesis.
See also ARTHRITIS; SKELETON.

JOINT (GEOLOGICAL) A joint, in geology, is a crack in a rock bed. There is no movement along joints, as there is along faults (see FAULT).

Joints are found in rocks whose surface can be seen. Joints always appear in groups. Often the joints in a certain group are parallel to each other, though they may run in any direction. Joints are found mostly at right angles to the rock bed. Joints in limestone are often made bigger by the action of groundwater. A horizontal pattern of joints called sheeting is often found in granite. The joints are close together near the surface but spread out below it. Finally, they disappear.
See also ROCK.

JOULE A joule is a unit used to measure energy or work. It is one of the units in the metric system (see METRIC SYSTEM). A joule is the work done when a force of one newton moves a distance of one meter in the direction of the force (one newton-meter) (see NEWTON). For example, it takes about one joule to raise a hamburger one meter from a table. In electricity, a joule is the work done by a current of one ampere flowing through a resistance of one ohm for one second (one watt-second) (see AMPERE; OHM; WATT). A joule equals 10 million ergs. *See also* JOULE, JAMES PRESCOTT.

JOULE, JAMES PRESCOTT (1818–1889)

James Joule was an English physicist. He was interested in different kinds of energy, especially heat and electricity. His first important experiment showed how water becomes warmer when it is stirred. He measured the exact amount of heat that was given off by a measured amount of work. This is called the mechanical equivalent of heat. He also measured the amount of heat given off by an electric current flowing through a wire (see HEAT).

Joule worked with Lord Kelvin to measure the way gases cool when they expand, or move outward (see KELVIN, LORD). This helped fix the absolute scale of temperature. It was also useful information to people building steam engines. Another measurement that Joule made was the speed at which gas molecules move. Means of measurement today have shown that his figures were very nearly correct. The joule, a unit of work, is named for him. *See also* JOULE.

JUNCO

A junco is a small sparrowlike bird that belongs to the bunting family (see SPARROW). There are several species of juncos in North America. All but the slate-colored junco live only in the West. The slate-colored junco, also called the dark-eyed junco, is common throughout the entire continent. It is a frequent visitor to bird feeders during the winter. The slate-colored junco is 5.25 in. [13 cm] long. It has a solid gray back and wings and a white belly. Juncos eat seeds.

JUNG, CARL GUSTAV

(yŏŏng, kärl gŏŏs´-täf) (1875–1961) Carl Jung was a Swiss psychologist and psychiatrist, a person who studies how people think and behave (see PSYCHIATRY; PSYCHOLOGY). He developed a system of psychology called analytical psychology. This is similar to psychoanalysis (see PSYCHOANALYSIS). However, analytical psychology places importance on different unconscious urges, things that cause people to act without thinking. These urges, according to Jung, form the basis of personality and mental health. Jung felt that dreams were a symbolic language through which we could better understand ourselves and our motivations. Jung invented the terms *introvert* and *extrovert* to describe kinds of personalities. An introvert is a person whose interests and understanding of life come mainly from his or her own thoughts and feelings. An extrovert is mainly motivated by interest in the things and people around him or her.

JUNIPER

Junipers are evergreen trees and shrubs belonging to the cypress family (see EVERGREEN). They are found in cooler areas of the Northern Hemisphere. Many of the 60 or so species have separate male and female plants. The female plant produces red or blue berrylike cones. The leaves are either needlelike in whorls around the branches, or scalelike and close to the stem (see LEAF). Common juniper is a short shrub found in many parts of the world. Its cones are used to flavor gin. Eastern red cedar is a juniper and not a true cedar. Its sweet-smelling, reddish wood is used in cedar chests and closets as well as in furniture, and is also used for making pencils. It is sometimes called pencil cedar (see CEDAR).

JUNIPER
Drooping juniper (left) is a small tree that can be found growing in dry regions of Texas. It has scalelike leaves (below).

JUPITER

Jupiter, the fifth planet from the sun, is the largest planet in the solar system. Jupiter is about 483,500,000 mi. [778,120,000 km] from the sun, and it comes as close as 390,000,000 mi. [628,000,000 km] to Earth. Jupiter has a diameter of about 88,700 mi. [142,700 km]. It takes Jupiter about twelve years to make one complete orbit (journey) around the sun. Jupiter also rotates (spins) on an axis (imaginary line passing through it) with only a 3° tilt. Jupiter spins the fastest of any of the planets, making a complete rotation (one spin) in nine hours and fifty-five minutes, compared with Earth's twenty-four hours. Because of this rapid spinning, Jupiter's poles are flattened, and its equator bulges (see EQUATOR; POLE).

The atmosphere of Jupiter consists almost entirely of hydrogen and helium, the two main gases that make up the sun. Less than 1 percent consists of other gases, such as methane, ammonia, and carbon monoxide. The atmosphere also has traces of water vapor. If Jupiter were eighty times heavier, it would be a star. This idea is supported by the fact that Jupiter gives off more energy than it receives (see STAR).

Jupiter has no surface. Its core is hidden by thick clouds that form colored bands around the planet. The clouds are made up of frozen ammonia and methane, among other things. Jupiter's atmosphere has a large, oval red spot. It is about 25,000 mi. [40,200 km] long and 20,000 mi. [32,000 km]

LARGEST PLANET
Jupiter is the largest planet in the solar system. Of the outer giant planets, it is nearest to the earth.

wide. The red spot is one of many spots that are cyclones in Jupiter's atmosphere. Jupiter is orbited by a thin ring consisting mostly of dust particles (see CYCLONE).

The temperature above Jupiter's clouds is about -66.2°F [-100°C]. At the core, the temperature is much higher, reaching 18,032°F [10,000°C] or more.

Jupiter has the largest mass of any planet. It is so great that 1,300 earths could fit into Jupiter. Jupiter has sixteen known moons. The four biggest, Io, Europa, Ganymede, and Callisto, were discovered in 1610 by the Italian astronomer Galileo (see GALILEO). In 1979, the first active volcano other than on the earth was discovered in photographs of Io taken by the *Voyager 1* space probe.

Several American space probes (spacecraft that carry no people) have studied Jupiter. *Pioneer X* in 1973 and *Pioneer-Saturn* in 1974 obtained new information on the largest planet. Then, in 1979, *Voyager 1* and *Voyager 2* sent back more information, including detailed photographs.

In 1992 the space probe *Ulysses* flew past Jupiter at a distance of 236,000 mi. [380,000 km]. This is just inside the orbit of 10, and closer than 11, of Jupiter's 16 moons.

In July 1994, nineteen fragments of a comet called Shoemaker-Levy collided with Jupiter. The fragments caused great explosions in Jupiter's atmosphere, equivalent to millions of tons of TNT. The explosions blew hot material 1,365 mi. [2,200 km] above the tops of the clouds.

See also PLANET; SOLAR SYSTEM; SPACE EXPLORATION.

Jupiter   Saturn   Uranus   Neptune   Pluto

JURASSIC PERIOD The Jurassic period in the earth's history began about 208 million years ago. It lasted about 61 million years.

Dinosaurs reached their greatest size during the Jurassic period. The first bird, *Archaeopteryx,* lived then (see ARCHAEOPTERYX; DINOSAUR). Other animals that lived during this time were squids, fish, and crocodiles and other reptiles that lived in water. There were also trees on which cones grew, as they do on pine trees. Gas, oil, gold, and uranium formed during the Jurassic period.
See also GEOLOGICAL TIME SCALE.

JUST, ERNEST EVERETT (1883–1941) Ernest Everett Just was an African-American biologist who pioneered research in cellular reproduction. Just was born in Charleston, South Carolina. He received a bachelor's degree from Dartmouth College in Hanover, New Hampshire, in 1907 and a doctoral degree in zoology and physiology from the University of Chicago in 1916. He spent much of his career teaching biology at Howard University in Washington, D.C.

Just investigated the structure of cells and believed the cell membrane was important in the development of cells (see CELL). Just said scientists should study the cell membrane and how it interacts with the substances inside the cell and the environment. This study could help explain evolution and the processes of life, such as growth and death (see EVOLUTION). In addition, Just experimented with the effects of ultraviolet radiation in the creation of cancer cells (see CANCER; ULTRAVIOLET RAY).

Just was often not allowed to research at American universities that had only white students and white professors, so he did much of his research and writing in Europe. His books include *The Biology of the Cell Surface.* In 1915, the National Association for the Advancement of Colored People (NAACP) awarded Just the first Spingarn Medal. The Spingarn Medal is awarded each year to the African-American who has done the most to advance his or her field.

JUTE Jute is a fiber that comes from two species of plants belonging to the genus *Corchorus.* These plants reach a height of 11.5 ft. [3.5 m] with yellow flowers at the top of the stem.

The jute fibers are released by soaking the cut stems in water until the softer parts disintegrate. This process is called retting. The fibers are soft and shiny and up to 8.25 ft. [2.5 m] long. They can be made into thread used for curtains, carpets, rope, twine, and burlap.
See also FIBER.

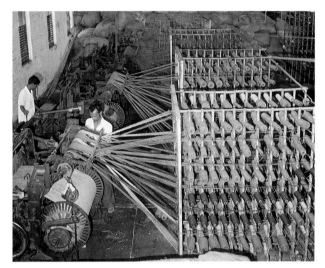

JUTE
These workers in a factory in Bangladesh are weaving jute fibers into backing for making carpets.

K

KANGAROO Kangaroos are Australian pouched mammals, or marsupials, belonging to the family Macropodidae (see MARSUPIAL). The family contains about 50 species, but only the biggest ones are normally called kangaroos. The others include wallabies, wallaroos, pademelons, tree kangaroos, and some very small species known as rat kangaroos (see WALLABY). Apart from some of the rat kangaroos, all kangaroos feed entirely on plants. The biggest species are the red kangaroo and the great gray kangaroo, or forester. The adult males of both species are called boomers. They stand about 6 ft. [1.8 m] high and weigh about 100 lb. [45 kg], although the largest ones reach a height of 7 ft. [2.1 m] and weigh over 150 lb. [68 kg]. The females, called fliers, are much smaller.

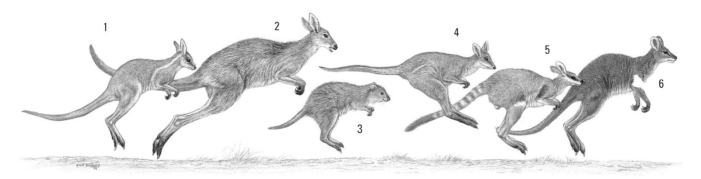

KANGAROO—Varieties

There are many species of kangaroos, some of which are called wallabies. Pictured here are (1) brindled nailtail wallaby; (2) wallaroo; (3) quokka; (4) red-legged pademelon; (5) yellow-footed rock wallaby; and (6) gray forest wallaby.

KANGAROO—Largest

The red kangaroo is the largest marsupial animal. It lives in open grasslands and semidesert areas of Australia.

All members of the kangaroo family are red, brown, or gray, and they are built similarly, although they differ greatly in size. All have large back legs and feet—the family name, macropod, actually means "big feet"—small front legs, and a stout tail that is often used as a seat when the animals are resting. The head is small and resembles that of a deer, which is not surprising because the animals graze and browse in the same way. When moving slowly, kangaroos use all four legs, but at other times they bound along on their back legs. They can reach speeds of 40 m.p.h. [64 kph] and can easily make high jumps of 6 ft. [1.8 m].

Gray kangaroos live mostly in the open forests and on the grasslands of southern Australia. Red kangaroos live on the dry grasslands and semi-desert areas in the center of the country. The animals are usually seen in small groups, but they sometimes form larger groups called mobs. They feed mainly in the evening and lie in the shade during the daytime.

Baby kangaroos are called joeys. A newborn joey measures only about 1 in. [2.5 cm] long and weighs about 0.035 oz [1 g]. It looks like a pink jellybean, and the only parts that are well developed are the forepaws. Immediately after birth, the joey uses these paws to drag itself from the birth canal up into its mother's pouch. It lives there on its mother's milk until it is six to eight months old.

Now that the doglike Tasmanian wolf, or thylacine, has been exterminated, the kangaroos have few enemies other than humans and the wild dogs called dingoes. Hunters have killed millions of kangaroos for their hides and meat. However, sheep farmers feel that there are still too many kangaroos because they compete with the sheep for grass.

KANGAROO RAT Kangaroo rats are tiny animals belonging to genus *Dipodomys* of the pocket mouse family, Heteromyidae. There are about 24 species. Kangaroo rats are rodents, just as squirrels, mice, and rats are. However, they jump around on long, powerful hind legs, much like kangaroos. Kangaroo rats grow to about 15 in. [38 cm] long, including a tail of 8 in. [20 cm]. They have short front legs, large heads, and big eyes. Their silky fur is yellow or brown on the upper parts, and white on the lower parts.

Kangaroo rats live in the deserts of the southwestern part of the United States. They nest in burrows (holes dug in the earth) and come out at night to feed on plants. Kangaroo rats do not have to drink water. They get water from the plants they eat. They can also produce water themselves from the dry seeds that they eat.

KANGAROO RAT
The kangaroo rat gets its name from its habit of standing on and jumping with its powerful back legs, much like a kangaroo.

KAOLIN Kaolin is a white clay that comes from feldspar that has decomposed (broken down) (see FELDSPAR). The word *kaolin* comes from a Chinese word meaning "high hill." Kaolin is also called china clay and porcelain clay. The chief sources of kaolin include Britain, Germany, France, China, Russia, and the United States.

Kaolin can be ground into a fine powder. When wet, this is easily worked and is made into pottery. Kaolin is also used in cloth, in rubber tires, and as a coating for paper.

KEKULÉ VON STRADONITZ, FRIEDRICH AUGUST (kā′koo lā fən shträ′ dō nĭts, frē′ drĭk ou′ goost) (1829–1896) Friedrich Kekulé was a German chemist. He added the name *von Stradonitz* later in his life. He is considered the father of modern organic chemistry (the chemistry of carbon compounds) (see COMPOUND; ORGANIC CHEMISTRY).

Kekulé was the first to develop diagrams that show the ways that atoms combine with each other to form chemical compounds. He developed the idea of valences (see ATOM; MOLECULE; VALENCE). An atom's valence determines its ability to combine with other atoms. Kekulé's diagrams showed that atoms join in particular geometrical patterns, such as lines and angles.

Kekulé also discovered the benzene ring (see BENZENE). He knew that benzene is a cluster of six carbon atoms. He tried to make a diagram that showed the structure of benzene. However, none of his diagrams fully accounted for the way that the benzene molecule behaved. Then Kekulé had a dream in which he saw the carbon atoms linked together in a ring, like a snake curled with its tail in its mouth. When Kekulé drew the benzene molecule in a circular arrangement, he found that it confirmed his idea that carbon has four valence powers, or combining powers. The arrangement also confirmed the ways that benzene was known to combine with other elements. Kekulé's diagram of the benzene ring is still sometimes used today. He also showed that carbon atoms can join other carbon atoms in only three predictable ways. These important discoveries helped other scientists study and develop many new kinds of chemicals based on carbon compounds.

KELVIN, LORD (1824–1907) Lord Kelvin was a scientist born in Scotland. His name was William Thomson and he was made a lord in 1892. He is known for his studies of heat and electricity. Lord Kelvin is most famous for discovering the temperature of absolute zero. He proved that at -459.67°F [-273.15°C], molecules would not move at all. This temperature is called absolute zero (see ABSOLUTE ZERO). The Kelvin temperature scale starts with absolute zero (see KELVIN SCALE).

Kelvin later stated his discovery in a different way. He said that "all energy finally runs down into heat." This is the idea of entropy and is also a way of stating the second law of thermodynamics. *See also* ENTROPY; THERMODYNAMICS.

LORD KELVIN
Lord Kelvin made fundamental discoveries about heat. The absolute temperate scale is measured in degrees Kelvin, named for the scientist.

KELVIN SCALE The Kelvin scale is a scale of temperature used for scientific measurements. The lowest point on the scale is zero. This is called absolute zero. This is a temperature impossible to obtain, though scientists have come very close to it (see ABSOLUTE ZERO). On the Kelvin scale, the freezing point of water is 273.15 K, and the boiling point is 373.15 K. The scale is named for the scientist Lord Kelvin. It is also called the absolute scale.

See also KELVIN, LORD.

KEPLER, JOHANNES (1571–1630) Johannes Kepler was a German astronomer, a scientist who studies stars and planets. He went to work under the Danish astronomer Tycho Brahe, in Prague, now in the Czech Republic, in 1600 (see BRAHE, TYCHO). When Brahe died in 1601, Kepler took his place as mathematician to the emperor, without pay. He was very poor for most of his life.

Kepler is famous for discovering the three laws of the planets' orbits (paths) around the sun. First, he discovered that the orbits of planets are elliptical (oval shaped) instead of round. Until then, planets had been thought to travel in circles. Then, Kepler discovered that an orbiting planet travels faster when it is nearer the sun. The third law says that a planet travels at an average speed that depends on its average distance from the sun. Planets farther from the sun travel more slowly. He discovered all this before most astronomers believed that the sun was the center of the solar system (see PLANET; SOLAR SYSTEM).

Kepler was a religious man. To him, his discoveries showed the harmony of God's creation. He lived at the same time as Galileo. The two men wrote to each other about their ideas. Many people disagreed with their discoveries.

See also GALILEO.

KERATIN Keratin is a tough material that forms the basis of animals' hair, feathers, scales, claws, nails, and hooves. Keratin is a protein (see PROTEIN). It is also found in the outer layer of skin called the stratum corneum, or horny layer. All these structures consist of dead cells in which

KERATIN
The huge horns of these ibexes have a bony core surrounded by layers of fibrous keratin.

keratin has largely replaced cytoplasm, the watery material between the cell nucleus and the cell membrane.

See also CELL; FEATHER; HAIR; NAIL; SKIN.

KEROSENE Kerosene is a light oil made from petroleum (see PETROLEUM). In 1854, Abraham Gesner, a Canadian geologist, first produced kerosene and gave it its name. At one time, lamps that burned kerosene were the chief source of artificial lighting.

Today, the chief use of kerosene is as a fuel in jet aircraft engines. In areas that are far from a source of electricity, kerosene is sometimes used for lighting and for cooking fuel. Kerosene is also used in some kinds of portable room heaters and as a fuel for farm machinery. Kerosene is also used in weed killers and insecticides.

Kerosene is a mixture of hydrocarbons. Hydrocarbons are compounds containing the elements hydrogen and carbon.

KESTREL A kestrel is a type of falcon. It belongs to the family Falconidae. Kestrels are found all over the world. In North America, they are known as sparrow hawks, but they are not true hawks. The

KESTREL

The American kestrel (left), often called the sparrow hawk, has brighter colors than its cousin from Europe and Asia (right).

American kestrel is small. It is only about 8.5 in. [22 cm] long—no bigger than a robin.
See also FALCON.

KETONE Ketones are organic (carbon-containing) chemical compounds (see COMPOUND). Ketones have molecules in which a carbonyl group of atoms (CO) is attached to the carbon atoms of two other groups of atoms. The simplest possible ketone is acetone. This has the formula CH_3COCH_3. It is also called dimethyl ketone (see ACETONE). Most ketones are colorless liquids that readily turn into vapors and have strong smells. Camphor is a ketone that forms crystals. Ketones have a number of uses in industry. They are used in the making of perfumes and as solvents (substances that can dissolve other substances) in the lacquer and plastics industries.

KIDNEY The kidneys are a vital pair of organs. They lie high up in the back of the abdomen, one on each side of the spine. They are partly overlapped by the lower ribs. The ribs help protect

them. The kidneys must be protected from damage because without them the body would quickly die. The function of the kidneys is to remove waste products from the bloodstream. The removal of waste products is called excretion. The kidneys are the main organs of excretion in all vertebrates (animals with backbones). They work as filters to purify the blood (see EXCRETION).

In human beings, the kidneys lie high up where the main artery of the body (the aorta) enters the abdomen. Each kidney is about 4 in. [10 cm] long, about 2.5 in. [6 cm] across, about 1 in. [2 cm] deep, and shaped like a kidney bean. The kidneys are dark red in color. Blood enters the kidneys through the renal arteries, which branch off the aorta. One renal artery goes to each kidney. Blood leaving the kidneys passes out through the renal veins. The filtered blood flows into the body's main veins, the venae cavae.

When blood enters a kidney through the renal artery, it travels to very small blood vessels called capillaries. The capillaries are arranged in tiny bunches like knots. Each knot is called a glomerulus. It has a small cup of tissue around it called a Bowman's capsule. From the capsule runs a coiled and twisting tubule (small tube) called a renal tubule. This joins with others like it and eventually forms a wider tube called a ureter. A ureter runs down from each kidney to the organ called the bladder.

A glomerulus in its capsule, together with its renal tubule, forms the unit known as a nephron. There are roughly one million nephrons in each kidney. The glomeruli (plural of *glomerulus*) are found in the cortex (outer layer) of the kidney. The renal tubules form loops in the darker, inner part of the kidney, called the medulla.

As blood passes through a glomerulus, it is filtered. Water, glucose, amino acids, and waste products are removed from the blood and collected by the renal tubule. The main waste product is the chemical called urea. Urea is formed from the breakdown of proteins in the body's tissues and as a product of digestion of protein that is eaten (see UREA). As the filtered fluid travels through the tubule to the ureter, water is absorbed from it back

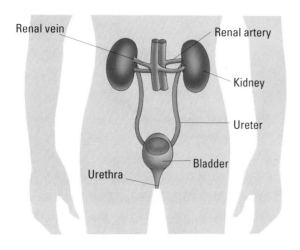

KIDNEY

The kidneys filter waste products and water from the bloodstream. Blood enters the kidney through the renal artery and leaves through the renal vein. Watery waste, in the form of urine, flows down the ureter and is stored in the bladder, before passing out of the body through the urethra.

into the bloodstream. Also taken back into the blood are the valuable molecules of glucose and amino acids. The body cannot afford to lose more water, glucose, and amino acids than necessary. The liquid that reaches the ureter is called urine. It is mainly a solution of urea and salt in water (see URINE).

Urine passes down the ureter and collects in the bladder. It is stored there until it is convenient to pass it to the outside. There are two ureters leading into the bladder, one ureter from each kidney. The single tube leading from the bladder to the outside is called the urethra.

During a day, the kidneys filter up to 53 gal. [200 liters] of blood. After the kidneys remove wastes from the blood, the purified blood reenters the circulatory system. Unless waste material is removed, it quickly builds up in the blood and acts as a poison to the entire body.

A person can survive with only one kidney. If one kidney is damaged or diseased, the other one usually grows in size to take over the work of the useless one. When both kidneys are damaged or diseased, the situation is serious. The patient must either have help from an artificial kidney machine (this process is called dialysis) or receive a transplanted kidney from a donor.

See also CIRCULATORY SYSTEM; DIALYSIS; MEDICAL ENGINEERING; TRANSPLANTATION.

KILN A kiln is an oven or furnace in which such things as pottery and bricks are fired (baked), dried, or melted. Kilns also are used to dry lumber, for roasting iron ores, for burning lime and dolomite, and in making Portland cement. Kilns are heated by electricity or by natural fuels. Some kilns reach temperatures of more than 2,192°F [1,200°C].

The common pottery kiln consists mainly of a clay chamber heated by flame from a furnace. Coal, gas, or oil serves as the fuel. A chimney provides a draft, drawing hot gases through the kiln. The flame does not touch the pottery, which has cases around it. Such kilns are called periodic or intermittent kilns. They have to be loaded, then heated, allowed to cool, and finally emptied.

In kilns called tunnel or continuous kilns, small rail cars carry the items to be fired, such as bricks, through a tunnel. The tunnel has its firing part in the center. Items dry and are fired as they pass this part. The items cool as they move away from this zone. Tunnel kilns can bake many items at once. *See also* CERAMICS.

KILN

Pottery is fired (baked) in a hot kiln to harden the clay that is used to make pottery.

KINETIC ENERGY Kinetic energy is the energy an object has because of its motion. A moving automobile has kinetic energy, for example. The kinetic energy of an object is calculated by multiplying half its mass by the square of its velocity (see MASS; VELOCITY).

Potential energy can change into kinetic energy, and kinetic energy can change into potential energy (see ENERGY; POTENTIAL ENERGY). For example, a car standing still at the top of a roller coaster track has potential energy but no kinetic energy. As it runs down the slope, the potential energy changes into kinetic energy. At the first dip in the track, most of the potential energy has been changed into kinetic energy. As the car begins to climb the opposite slope, the kinetic energy changes back into potential energy. However, the car will now have less potential energy than at the start because some energy has been lost by friction (see FRICTION). When the car reaches the top of the second slope, its kinetic energy will again be zero. When it races

down the other side, its kinetic energy builds up again.

Heat is a form of kinetic energy. In a gas, for example, the atoms and molecules move about freely. The temperature of the gas is a measure of the average kinetic energy of its atoms and molecules.

See also HEAT.

PROJECT 35

KINETIC THEORY According to the kinetic theory, all states of matter are made up of constantly moving, tiny particles called atoms or molecules (combinations of atoms) (see ATOM; MOLECULE). Empty space lies between these atoms or molecules. As the molecules or atoms of a gas move through space, they often collide, or run into each other. Molecules or atoms of a liquid act in the same way. However, liquid molecules or atoms do not move as fast or as far as gas molecules. Molecules or atoms of a solid move around a fixed point.

Because the atoms and molecules are moving, they possess kinetic energy. The amount of kinetic energy that any one particle possesses depends on its mass and velocity (see KINETIC ENERGY). An increase in temperature causes an increase in the average velocity of particles in a body. For example, the molecules of warm water move with greater velocity, and therefore have a higher average kinetic energy, than the molecules of cold water.

See also GAS.

KINGDOM A kingdom is the largest unit or division of living things. In the past, many scientists used a two-kingdom system in which animals belonged to the animal kingdom and plants belonged to the plant kingdom (see ANIMAL KINGDOM; PLANT KINGDOM).

New features of the many forms of life continue to be discovered by scientists. As a result, many taxonomists (scientists who specialize in classifying living things) came to feel that the two-kingdom system was inadequate. Several other systems have been proposed. Although there is no universal agreement, the five-kingdom system is the now most widely accepted.

ACTIVITY *How to use kinetic energy*

Tie a stone to each end of a piece of string about 2 ft. [60 cm] long. Place one stone on a table near the edge and drop the other stone off the other edge. The kinetic energy of the falling stone pulls the other stone off the table.

In the five-kingdom system, the animal kingdom includes all many-celled animals. The plant kingdom includes all many-celled plants. The fungus kingdom includes all types of fungi. Kingdom Protista, also called Protoctista, includes protozoans (one-celled, animallike organisms) and all algae except blue-green algae. Kingdom Monera, also called Prokaryotae, includes bacteria and blue-green algae.

See also CLASSIFICATION OF LIVING ORGANISMS; TAXONOMY.

KINGFISHER A kingfisher is a bird that belongs to the family Alcedinidae. It is a stocky bird with a large head and bill. Most of the eighty species of kingfishers are brightly colored. About half the species actually catch fish. The rest eat insects and small reptiles. In North America, there are two species: the belted kingfisher, which is widespread, and the green kingfisher of the United States-Mexico border area. Both these birds fish by diving headfirst into the water and catching the fish

KINGFISHER

The belted kingfisher of North America can raise a crest of feathers on its head.

in their bills. The belted kingfisher is about 12 in. [30 cm] long. It nests in sandbanks near streams.

KIRCHHOFF, GUSTAV ROBERT

(1824–1887) Gustav Kirchhoff was a German physicist. Kirchhoff worked with the German chemist Robert Bunsen. They discovered that the light that a very hot gas gives off is different from the light from a very hot solid or liquid. Solids and liquids give off light that contains many colors of the spectrum (see SPECTRUM). Gases give off only a few colors. Kirchhoff invented a machine called a spectroscope to learn about the light (see SPECTROSCOPE). He found that each gas gives off a different set of colors. These show as lines, called emission lines, on the spectrograph (picture made by a spectroscope). Another part of this discovery is that cool gases take in the same colors as they give off when they are hot. In place of the colored emission lines, dark absorption lines are formed when white light is passed through a cool gas into a spectroscope. In this way, cool gases can be identified. It is the emission spectrum from the sun and stars that make it possible for scientists to know what they are made of.

In addition to this work, Kirchhoff also worked with electricity. He stated two laws about electric circuits, known as Kirchhoff's laws. The first law is about networks of wires, in which wires carrying electric current meet at a point. The law states that the amount of current flowing into any point equals the amount of current flowing away from it. This is true no matter how many wires meet at the point.

Kirchhoff's second law is about closed electric circuits. It states that the electromotive forces in a circuit are equal to the currents multiplied by the resistances in each part of the circuit.

See also CIRCUIT, ELECTRIC; CURRENT, ELECTRIC; ELECTROMOTIVE FORCE; RESISTANCE, ELECTRICAL.

KIWI The kiwi is a bird that belongs to the family Apterygidae. It is about the size of a large chicken. None of the three species of kiwis can fly. The birds have wings, but they are small and hidden by hairlike feathers that cover the body. Kiwis

KIWI

The kiwi cannot fly but can run quickly through the New Zealand forest on its powerful, stubby legs.

live in the damp forests of New Zealand. They feed at night on earthworms and other small animals. Because the forests of New Zealand are being cleared, the kiwis are becoming scarce.

KIWI FRUIT The kiwi fruit, also known as the Chinese gooseberry, is a berry that is fuzzy, greenish brown, and about the size of a large chicken egg (see BERRY). It grows on a vine. The inside of the berry is green with small black seeds. Both the berry and the seeds can be eaten. Kiwi fruit has a tart but sweet taste, similar to strawberries, and is high in vitamin C. Once rarely seen in grocery stores in the United States, it has become a popular fruit.

KIWI FRUIT

A circle of small, black seeds creates a pattern inside the kiwi fruit. The fruit is also called Chinese gooseberry.

Kiwi fruit originated in China and was brought to New Zealand by 1906. It was planted there widely in the 1950s. Since the 1950s, France, the United States, Italy, Spain, and Japan have all produced increasing amounts of kiwi fruit. In the United States, kiwi fruit is harvested in October but kept in cold storage for marketing through April. Kiwi fruit that is sold in the United States from about April to October is imported. Each kiwi plant is either male or female. A one-acre field of 150 to 200 vines requires one male plant for every eight female plants. Bees transfer the pollen from the male to the female plants.

See also FRUIT; POLLINATION.

KNOT The knot is a unit of speed used at sea. It is equal to one nautical mile per hour. The international (U.S.) nautical mile is equal to 1.15 mi. [1.85 km]. *Knot* comes from the old method of measuring speed at sea. Sailors counted the number of knots in a rope thrown out over the stern, let out in a given time.

KOALA The koala is an Australian mammal that eats only the leaves of the eucalyptus tree. Although often called koala bear, Australian teddy bear, and native sloth, the koala is neither a bear nor a sloth. It is a marsupial (animal with a pouch) and related to the kangaroo (see MARSUPIAL). Unlike the kangaroo and most other pouched mammals, however, the koala's pouch opens toward the rear.

The koala is 24 to 34 in. [60 to 85 cm] long and weighs 11 to 16.5 lb. [5 to 7.5 kg]. It has gray fur on most of its body and yellowish fur on its belly. It has a small snout with a round nose that feels like leather. The koala has short legs with clawed feet. It has almost no tail at all. The koala sleeps during the day and eats at night.

A female koala gives birth to one baby, called a cub, every two years. Shortly after birth, the tiny cub enters its mother's pouch, where it stays for six months. It then crawls onto its mother's back, where it stays for another six months. The koala is full grown when it is two years old but not really mature until it is four years old. Koalas live for about twenty to thirty years.

KOALA

The koala is a slow-moving animal that comes out at night to feed on the leaves of eucalyptus trees.

Koalas are gentle, friendly animals. In the past, they were easy prey for hunters who wanted their fur. Koalas are now protected by law, but numbers are still decreasing as a result of loss of habitat and a disease that has killed off large numbers of the animals. The Australian government allows koalas to be exported only to the San Diego Zoo and the San Francisco Zoo in the United States. These are the only two zoos in the world where the proper kind of eucalyptus tree can be grown.

KOCH, ROBERT (1843–1910) Robert Koch was a German doctor. He began the study of bacteriology and invented many methods for studying bacteria. Koch discovered how to get pure cultures (samples) of bacteria. He also found dyes for staining bacteria so that they could be seen under the microscope.

With his methods, Koch discovered eleven different bacteria that cause diseases, including tuberculosis (1882) and Asiatic cholera (1883). He also researched malaria, rinderpest (cattle plague), bubonic plague, and sleeping sickness. Koch developed a test for diagnosing tuberculosis in 1890.

In 1905, Koch received the Nobel Prize for medicine.

See also BACTERIA.

KODIAK BEAR The Kodiak bear is a variety of Alaskan brown bear (see BROWN BEAR). It is the largest of the bears and the largest living land carnivore, or meat-eating animal. It may weigh as much as 1,650 lb. [750 kg] and be as tall as 9 ft. [2.7 m] when standing on its back legs. The Kodiak bear is found only on Kodiak Island in the Gulf of Alaska.

KODIAK BEAR

The Kodiak bear, found on Kodiak Island off Alaska, is the world's largest meat-eating animal on land.

KOLA NUT The kola nut is the seed of one of two evergreen trees of the genus *Cola* (see EVERGREEN). These trees belong to the cocoa family and are naturally found in Africa near the equator but are cultivated elsewhere as well. They grow to be about 40 ft. [12 m] tall. Clusters of small, yellow flowers produce leatherlike fruits. Each of these fruits contains several juicy kola nuts, each of which measures about 2 in. [5 cm] in diameter.

Kola nuts are used in making cola soft drinks and certain medicines. The nuts contain small amounts of the stimulant drugs caffeine and theobromine. *See also* CAFFEINE; STIMULANT.

KOMODO DRAGON The Komodo dragon is the largest living lizard on Earth. It belongs to the family Varanidae. Komodo dragons are one of the so-called monitor lizards and are found only on a few islands in Indonesia (see MONITOR LIZARD). *Komodo* is the name of one of the Indonesian islands where it is found.

The Komodo dragon has a long, flat body that may reach 10 ft. [2.8 m] in length and 300 lb. [136 kg] in weight. The tail of the lizard is as long as the

KOMODO DRAGON

The Komodo dragon is the world's largest lizard. It is named for one of the islands of Indonesia where it is found.

body and is very powerful. Young Komodo dragons eat insects, birds, and rodents. Adults are primarily scavengers and eat dead deer, monkeys, and wild pigs. The Komodo dragon does not normally bother humans, but it can be very dangerous if it is bothered by them.

KOOKABURRA

The laughing kookaburra is also known as the laughing jackass because of its loud, strange call.

KOOKABURRA A kookaburra is a bird that belongs to the kingfisher family, Alcedinidae (see KINGFISHER). There are two species: the laughing kookaburra and the blue-winged kookaburra. Both species live in Australia. They are about 17 in. [42.5 cm] long with very large heads and bills. The feathers of the kookaburra are mostly white with black, brown, and blue on the wings. Kookaburras eat insects, frogs, lizards, mice, and occasionally fish

that they catch by diving into the water. They also catch a large number of snakes.

KREBS CYCLE

The Krebs cycle is an important series of chemical reactions. The reactions take place inside living cells in organisms called aerobes (see AEROBE). The reactions release energy. All cells need energy to stay alive and do their work. The energy comes from the chemical compounds that make up food. Food acts as fuel.

A gasoline engine oxidizes, or burns, its fuel very rapidly. All the energy is suddenly released as heat. Cells cannot work this way. They must oxidize their fuel very slowly. The main fuel that they use is the sugar glucose. This can be oxidized in gentle stages to form, eventually, carbon dioxide, water, and energy stored in the form of ATP (adenosine triphosphate) (see ATP).

The cells first change glucose into pyruvic acid through the process of glycolysis, which is not part of the Krebs cycle. The pyruvic acid is then broken down further in the Krebs cycle reactions, which produce carbon dioxide and water as wastes. The energy obtained during the reactions is stored in molecules of ATP. The Krebs cycle reactions usually take place inside tiny structures inside cells called mitochondria (see MITOCHONDRIA). The reactions are made to work by special substances called enzymes (see ENZYME). The energy stored from the Krebs cycle reactions can be used later wherever it is needed. Other names for the Krebs cycle include the citric acid cycle and the tricarboxylic acid cycle. *See also* CELL; GLUCOSE; METABOLISM; RESPIRATION.

KRILL

Krill is a name for a group of small, shrimplike animals that live in seas throughout the world, although they are most common in cold waters. Krill make up the order Euphausiacea in the class Crustacea (see CRUSTACEAN). There are more than ninety species of krill. They range in length from 0.37 to 6 in. [10 to 150 mm].

Krill have special organs that give off light. Scientists believe that krill use these organs to avoid enemies or to attract a mate. Krill do not like sunlight. Many species stay in the dark depths of the sea during daylight hours. They move to the surface to feed at night. Krill swim in groups of millions called swarms.

Many kinds of fish, seals, squid, water birds, and baleen whales feed on krill. In antarctic and subarctic ocean areas, baleen whales depend almost entirely on krill for food (see WHALE).

In the 1960s, Japanese and Soviet scientists began to study krill as a possible important source of protein for human beings. Some of these scientists now believe that the number of an antarctic species, *Euphausia superba*, is great enough to support a large fishery in Antarctica. Other people fear that if humans begin to eat krill, this would harm ocean animals that depend on krill for food.

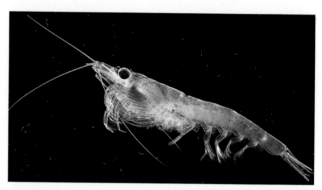

KRILL
Shrimplike krill provide food for fish and other animals that live in the sea.

KRYPTON

(krĭp′ tŏn′) Krypton is a gas without color or smell. It is an element, and it is one of the family of inert gases, like helium and argon (see ELEMENT; INERT GAS). Its symbol is Kr.

Krypton is used in fluorescent lights and certain electronic tubes. It is inert—that is, it does not react readily with other substances. Krypton is obtained by the distillation of liquid air (see DISTILLATION). The element was discovered by the British chemist Sir William Ramsay in 1898 (see RAMSAY, SIR WILLIAM). Krypton has the atomic number 36, and its relative atomic mass is 83.80. Krypton boils at -242.1°F [-152.3°C] and melts at -249.9°F [-156.6°C].

KUDZU

Kudzu is a fast-growing, flowering vine that is common in the southeastern United States. Kudzu belongs to the pea family (see PEA FAMILY). Kudzu grows up to 12 in. [30 cm] a day. It sometimes

KUDZU

Kudzu grows so fast that it can soon completely cover a building with its bright green foliage.

grows as long as 100 ft. [30 m]. Its thick, starchy roots grow down to 12 ft. [3.6 m]. Kudzu has wide, three-pointed leaves and purple flowers. Its fruit is a hairy legume that grows up to 4 in. [10 cm] in diameter (see FRUIT; LEGUME).

Kudzu was first brought to the United States in the late 1800s from China and Japan. The Chinese and Japanese eat the roots and make a fiber from the stems (see FIBER). At first, people in the United States used kudzu for decoration and to feed livestock. In the 1930s, farmers began to plant kudzu as a cover crop. A cover crop replenishes nutrients and protects the soil from erosion (see EROSION). However, because kudzu grows so fast and is difficult to get rid of, many people now consider kudzu a problem. Kudzu often completely covers buildings and trees.

L

LACEWING Lacewings are small insects belonging to the order Neuroptera. They have two pairs of wings with fine networks of lacelike veins. There are two families of lacewings: the green lacewings and the brown lacewings.

The green lacewings (family Chrysopidae) are sometimes called golden eyes because of the color of their eyes. They have slender green bodies and long, thin antennae (see ANTENNAE). The female

lays her eggs at the ends of threads of mucus. The threads harden on contact with the air, so each egg has its own stalk. This makes it more difficult for some predators to get at the eggs. The larva is yellowish gray and has large, sharp jaws. It uses these jaws to capture and kill soft-bodied insects. It then sucks the fluids from the bodies of its prey. Since its favorite food is the aphid, the lacewing larva is sometimes called an aphid-lion. After about two weeks, the larva spins a cocoon, inside which it turns into a pupa (see COCOON). It takes another two weeks for the insect to pass through the pupal stage and become an adult. The green lacewing is sometimes called stinkfly because it gives off a foul smell for protection.

The brown lacewings (family Hemerobiidae) are smaller than the green lacewings. They sometimes have spots on their wings, and the females do not lay their eggs on stalks.

See also INSECT.

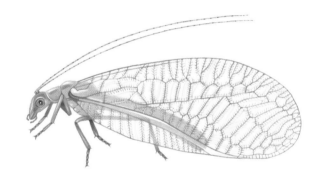

LACEWING

The green lacewing has gold-colored eyes and antennae (feelers) that are longer than its body.

LACQUER Lacquer is a shiny, protective coating used on metal, wood, paper, and porcelain. It is made from compounds of resin, cellulose, or lac. Lac is a sticky substance given off by certain insects (see CELLULOSE; RESIN; SCALE INSECT). Lacquers are made in all the colors commonly found in paints.

Lacquer made with resin is called a true spirit varnish. The resin is usually mixed with turpentine. The turpentine evaporates when exposed to air, leaving only the coating of resin on the material. When a cellulose compound is used to make lacquer, the compound is usually dissolved in butyl alcohol, which also evaporates when exposed to air.

Ethyl alcohol is the evaporating solution used for lacquer made from lac.

In Japan and China, a natural lacquer is obtained from the lacquer, or varnish, tree. Sap from the tree is collected, strained, and treated with heat. The result is a thick, dark brown, syrupy liquid. The liquid is diluted, and sometimes colored, before being used as a lacquer.

Modern lacquers are used to put finishing coats on thousands of materials. The paper industry uses clear and colored lacquers to finish packages, labels, and book covers. Lacquers are used in the furniture industry as a final waterproof coating. They also provide the high-gloss finish on automobiles. Acrylic-resin lacquers make an excellent coating for polished metals, such as brass and chromium. *See also* ACRYLIC; VARNISH.

LACTIC ACID

Lactic acid is the acid that gives sour milk its sour taste. It is an organic acid—that is, it contains carbon. Lactic acid is important in the body. It is formed during the breakdown of glucose (a sugar) in the muscles when there is little oxygen to spare because of increased bodily demand. Its formula is $CH_3 \cdot CH(OH) \cdot COOH$.

As a rule, in the body's cells, glucose is first changed into pyruvic acid. The pyruvic acid is then broken down further as part of the Krebs cycle. Energy is released, and carbon dioxide and water are produced as wastes (see KREBS CYCLE). The reactions of the Krebs cycle require oxygen.

When there is not enough oxygen in the body for this reaction to take place, pyruvic acid may be changed to lactic acid instead, in a reaction that does not require oxygen and that releases energy quickly. When a person exercises strenuously, the muscles use up oxygen rapidly. If the blood cannot supply enough oxygen, then lactic acid is formed. This supplies energy to keep the muscles working without oxygen. However, this builds up an "oxygen debt." Oxygen must be "paid back" by the blood to get rid of the lactic acid later. This is why a person pants for a while after hard exercise. The lactic acid in the muscles is probably also the reason for the aching and heavy feeling that a person may feel after hard exercise.

Lactic acid is used in the dyeing industry. It is also important in the production of cheese and yogurt. *See also* ACID.

LADYBUG

The ladybug, or ladybird beetle, is any of about five thousand species of small, oval beetles belonging to the family Coccinellidae of the order Coleoptera (see BEETLE). These insects are usually bright red or yellow with black markings. They are about 0. 1 to 0.3 in. [1 to 7 mm] long and have short legs and tough outer wings. They are usually thought of as helpful insects because they feed on large numbers of insects that humans consider pests, such as plant lice and scale insects. Ladybugs are frequently placed in areas where there are a lot of such insects (see BIOLOGICAL CONTROL). A few species, however, are considered pests themselves, because they cause damage to certain crops.

The ladybug larva is usually gray with bright or pale spots. It feeds on aphids (plant lice) and other insects. The process of metamorphosis is completed within a month (see METAMORPHOSIS). Before the winter, large numbers of ladybugs gather in protected places to hibernate (see HIBERNATION).

The ladybug gets its name from the fact that in the Middle Ages, farmers discovered the importance of this beetle to their crops. They dedicated the beetle to the Virgin Mary and called it "the beetle of Our Lady."

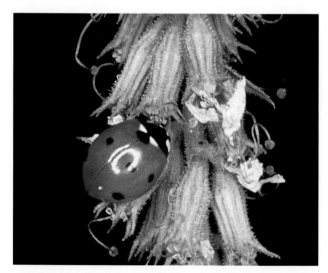

LADYBUG
Ladybugs are small, oval, usually brightly colored beetles. There are more than five thousand different species. Ladybugs often feed on such harmful insects as plant lice.

LAKES AND PONDS

Lakes and ponds are bodies of water. Although they often have slight currents, they do not flow as a river or stream does. It might be said that lakes and ponds are holes in the earth that are filled with water. People often think of a pond just as a small lake. However, limnologists—scientists who study freshwater lakes, ponds, and rivers—use the term *pond* for any still body of water that is shallow enough to allow sunlight to reach the bottom. Plants and algae can grow on the bottom of a pond but cannot grow on the bottom of a lake. There is no light there.

Lakes and ponds are formed in many different ways. Sometimes, a hole is formed in the earth by shifts in the earth's crust. When such a hole fills with water, a lake is formed. Lake Okeechobee in Florida and Lake Tahoe in California were formed in this way. Lake Baikal in Russia, the deepest lake in the world, was formed in a crack of the earth's crust. Other lakes form in the open tops of old volcanoes. Crater Lake in Oregon is this kind of lake (see VOLCANO). Wind can create or destroy lakes by blowing soil across a river or stream, forming a dam. Landslides often dam a river or stream, making a lake behind it. Humans also deliberately create lakes and ponds by building dams across rivers and streams (see DAM; LANDSLIDE). Meteorites often make large holes in the ground when they strike the earth. Lakes may later form in these holes (see METEOR).

Probably the most common cause of lakes, however, is glaciers (see GLACIATION). Thousands of years ago, huge ice sheets moved south from the North Pole. These ice sheets were over a mile thick in some places. They were so heavy that they pushed down the face of the earth (see ISOSTASY). As they moved, they dug holes in the earth, plowed gravel and sand into hills, and carved holes in mountains. As the ice melted, water filled many of these holes and low areas. The Great Lakes, located between the United States and Canada, were formed in this way.

What lakes and ponds are like depends on the area where they are found. For example, lakes in Alaska are mostly cold, clear, and rocky, with trout and few plants. On the other hand, lakes in Louisiana are mostly warm, murky, and muddy, with catfish and many plants. Although most lakes are freshwater, some have salt in them because of the soil around them. For example, the Great Salt Lake in Utah has more salt in its waters than the waters of the oceans do.

Lakes do not last forever. They may fill up with silt from rivers which drain into them (see SILT). At

FRESHWATER LAKE

A lake provides a habitat for many plants and animals. But lakes can easily become polluted by chemicals washed off surrounding land.

other times, an earthquake, hurricane, or glacier may break open the side of a lake and drain it. Not many lakes last more than 100,000 years.

See also ECOSYSTEM; RIVER; SUCCESSION.

LAKE LIFE

A clean freshwater lake can support a wide range of life, from plants and insects to fish, amphibians, birds, and mammals. Plants and animals that live permanently in water are known as aquatic organisms.

LAMARCK, JEAN BAPTISTE (1744–1829)

Jean Baptiste Lamarck was a French naturalist. As a young man, he wanted to study medicine but was too poor. He joined the army when he was seventeen and later became a bank clerk. His first work in natural history was a book on the plants of France.

Lamarck became keeper of plants at the Jardin du Roi (King's Garden), which is now the famous Jardin des Plantes (Garden of Plants). In 1793, he was made professor of "insects and worms" at the new Paris Museum of Natural History. One of his duties was to classify the collection. While he was doing this, he developed a theory of evolution. At that time, fossils (remains of something once alive) were listed apart from living things. They were supposed to be part of an earlier set of God's creations that were wiped out in the Flood described in the Bible. Lamarck had heard about Hutton's ideas of geological change. He decided that animals changed in order to adapt themselves as the face of the earth changed. He was not quite right in the way he thought that this happened. However, his idea that evolution happened at all was very new and important.

JEAN BAPTISTE LAMARCK
Jean Baptiste Lamarck put forward early theories about evolution. Although his theories were not quite correct, they helped other scientists develop ideas about evolution.

Lamarck thought that changes of shape that took place during an animal's life could be passed on to its children. In other words, if a giraffe stretches its neck while reaching to eat leaves on high branches, then its babies will have longer necks. This idea is called the inheritance of acquired characteristics. Scientists now know that most evolution happens by a process called natural selection.

See also EVOLUTION.

LAMPREY

A lamprey is an eellike fish that belongs to the family Petromyzontidae. It is one of the most primitive kinds of vertebrates (animals with backbones). Lampreys do not have jaws or bones. Their skeletons are made up of cartilage instead of bone (see CARTILAGE). Adult lampreys range in length from 6 to 40 in. [15 to 100 cm]. They have a large suckerlike mouth armed with circular rows of horny teeth. They also have seven round gill openings, through which they get oxygen, along each side of their head (see GILLS). Lampreys have fins on the back and the tail, but none on the sides.

Many of the 30 or so species of lampreys in the world are parasites. They fasten themselves to other animals to feed on their blood and other tissues (see PARASITE). However, only four of the fourteen species found in North America are parasites. The other ten species live in the mud of freshwater streams and feed on small animals. All lampreys spawn (lay their eggs) in freshwater streams (see SPAWNING). The young lampreys, called ammocoetes, live in the mud and feed on microscopic animals for up to four years before reaching maturity. Most lampreys stay in freshwater all their lives,

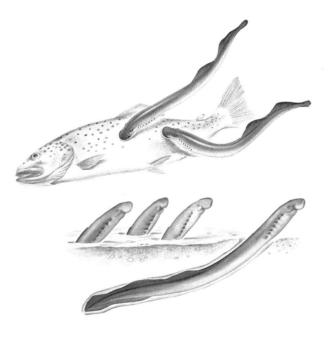

LAMPREY
Brook lampreys (top) use their sucker mouths to eat the flesh of trout. Young freshwater lampreys (above) are larvae that resemble eels. They live in a burrow on the bottom and feed by filtering food particles from the water.

but the parasitic species generally move to the sea when they grow up. They spend two or three years feeding on other sea fishes before returning to the freshwater streams to spawn and die.

When the Welland Canal was built around Niagara Falls in 1829, the sea lamprey was able to move into the upper Great Lakes. In these lakes, the sea lamprey does not return to the sea anymore. It uses the lakes as it would the ocean. It spawns in the rivers that flow into the lakes. Since the lamprey had never been present in the Great Lakes before, it did not have any enemies or diseases there, and its numbers increased. The sea lamprey feeds like other parasitic lampreys. It attaches itself to the side of a fish with its suckerlike mouth. It chews a hole in the fish's side with its pointed teeth and slowly sucks the blood out of its victim, which then often dies. The lamprey nearly wiped out the lake trout. Poisons that kill only lampreys have now been discovered. Their use has cut down the numbers of lampreys in the Great Lakes.
See also FISH.

LANDSLIDE A landslide occurs when a large mass of soil and rock tumbles down a slope. It may cause great damage and loss of life. In 1920, a landslide in China killed about 200,000 people.

A slump landslide takes place when the earth at the bottom of a slope is removed. This may be caused by waves undercutting the foot of a cliff (see EROSION). Mudflows are downward movements of soil and loose rock soaked with water. A lahar is a landslide of water-soaked volcanic material (see VOLCANO).

Landslides may crash into lakes, causing waves that may overflow a dam. Landslides may also block rivers to form dams.

LANTHANIDE (lăn′ thə nīd′) The lanthanide elements follow the element lanthanum in the periodic table (see PERIODIC TABLE, VOL. 23). They are any one of a group of elements with atomic numbers from element 58, which is cerium, to element 71, which is lutetium. They all have similar properties and most are silver-gray metals.

LANDSLIDE

Landslides take place when large masses of rock and soil tumble down a slope. Landslides are capable of causing great damage. They have killed thousands of people, damaged or destroyed buildings, blocked rivers, and caused lakes to overflow their dams.

The lanthanide elements have many scientific and industrial uses. They are used to make lamps, lasers, magnets, and X-ray intensifying screens. Others, such as gadolinium, are used as phosphors, the materials that make the colors in a television screen. Some lanthanide elements are added to different metals, such as aluminum and magnesium, to make them stronger. Others are used as catalysts in various manufacturing processes in the petroleum and chemical industries (see CATALYST).

LAPIS LAZULI (lăp′ ĭs lăz′ yə lē) Lapis lazuli is a beautiful, deep blue mineral that is used as a gemstone. It can be cut and polished to make jewelry and other ornaments. Lapis lazuli is sometimes called lazurite. Lapis lazuli may also contain pyrite, which shows as tiny, shining spots. These spots help people identify real lapis lazuli. Chemically, lapis lazuli is chiefly made up of aluminum, sodium, sulfur, and silica. Pyrite consists of iron and sulfur. Lapis lazuli is found in masses of fine grains or crystals, usually in limestone. Lapis lazuli is mined mainly in Afghanistan,

LAPIS LAZULI

This necklace is made from beads of lapis lazuli, a deep blue mineral that can be polished and used as a gemstone.

California, Chile, and Russia. Afghanistan has produced the best specimens of this mineral (see CRYSTAL; MINERAL).

In powdered form, lapis lazuli was once the only source of ultramarine, a blue pigment (coloring material) used in artists' paints. Most ultramarine is now synthetic (human made). In ancient times, people believed that lapis lazuli had value as a medicine. They ground the mineral into a powder, which they mixed with milk. This mixture was used as a dressing for sores.

LAPLACE, PIERRE SIMON (1749–1827)

Pierre Simon Laplace was a French mathematician and astronomer. He came from a poor farming family, but by the age of 18 had mastered what was then known in mathematics. He obtained a post at the Paris Military School, then occupied several official posts and wrote numerous papers on astronomy and mathematics.

For almost thirty years, Laplace made the majority of the advances in astronomical theory of his time. Between 1799 and 1825, he published in five volumes his great work, the *Mécanique Céleste*, which incorporated all that had been done in astronomy since the time of Newton (1642–1727) (see ASTRONOMY; NEWTON, SIR ISAAC). His work included tidal theory, the study of planetary orbits, and the long-term stability of the solar system. He also published works on which nearly all later developments in the theory of probability are based.

Laplace survived and prospered in the French Revolution, and even discussed astronomy with Napoleon. After the Revolution, Laplace was honored by being made a marquis. His great works in math and science inspired many others. Yet on his deathbed Laplace said, "What we know is minute; what we are ignorant of is vast."

LARCH A larch is a coniferous tree that is a member of the pine family, Pinaceae (see CONIFER; PINE FAMILY). Unlike other members of this family, the larch is not an evergreen. It is a deciduous tree. The whorled, needlelike leaves fall to the ground in the autumn. The tree spends the winter without

leaves (see DECIDUOUS TREE; EVERGREEN). There are ten species of larch in the world. There is only one species of larch that is native to North America. It is most often called a tamarack. The European larch has also been planted in North America. Larches prefer wet, spongy soils that have acid in them. They are important timber trees.

LARCH

The larch is an unusual member of the pine family because it sheds its needle-shaped leaves in the winter.

LARK The lark is a bird that belongs to the family Alaudidae. It is common in open grasslands. Larks rarely perch on a tree or shrub. They nest on the ground and eat seeds and insects. Male larks are often seen flying high in the air over fields while they sing a high-pitched song. There are over seventy species in the world, but only one species—the horned lark—is native to North America. It is about 6.5 in. [16.25 cm] long. The horned lark's "horns" are two black tufts of feathers that protrude above its head.

LARK

The bar-tailed desert lark lives in the deserts of northern Africa and the Middle East, where it feeds on seeds and insects.

LARVA A larva is an immature stage in the life history of an animal. It occurs between birth (or hatching) and adulthood and usually differs from the adult in activity, environment, appearance, and eating habits. For example, sessile, or nonmoving, organisms may have a larva that is mobile and free-swimming. This allows the organism to become more widely distributed. The sponge, for instance, produces a free-swimming, ciliated larva (see CILIUM; SPONGE).

Some terrestrial, or land-dwelling, animals have aquatic, or water-dwelling, larvae. Adult amphibians spend part of their time on land and breathe through lungs, but amphibian larvae are aquatic. Frogs and toads, for example, have aquatic larvae called tadpoles, or polliwogs (see AMPHIBIAN).

Most insects have a larval form that does not look anything like the adult. The larvae never have wings and many of them have special names. Caterpillars, for example, are the larvae of butterflies and moths, and maggots are the larvae of flies. Many larvae have different eating habits from the adults. A caterpillar, for example, chews leaves, but when it turns into a butterfly or a moth, it sucks nectar (a sweet liquid produced by many flowers) (see CATERPILLAR). Mosquito larvae live in water and feed on microscopic organisms, while the adults fly in the air and feed on blood and nectar (see INSECT).

The change from larval form to adult form is

Larva (caterpillar)

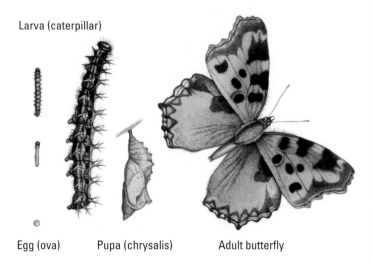

Egg (ova)   Pupa (chrysalis)   Adult butterfly

LARVA

A butterfly larva, or caterpillar, sheds its skin several times as it grows, before changing into a pupa, or chrysalis.

called metamorphosis. It takes place quite gradually in frogs and toads, with the tadpoles slowly developing legs and losing their tails as they grow up. Insect larvae do not gradually change into adults. They turn into pupae first. During this stage their bodies are completely broken down and rebuilt in the adult form.

See also CHRYSALIS; METAMORPHOSIS; PUPA.

 PROJECT 66

LARYNX The larynx is the part of the throat through which air passes. It is also called the voice box. When a person breathes, air passes through the larynx down from the mouth and nose. It then passes into the trachea (windpipe) and from there into the lungs. The larynx is part of the air passages, and it acts as a valve to protect the lower air passages from food and other swallowed objects. The larynx is specially designed to produce the voice. The larynx is boxlike, with walls of tough cartilage (see CARTILAGE). Inside, two folds of tissue lie along the sides, with a gap between them. These are the vocal cords. When a person breathes quietly, the cords are loose, and the gap between them is wide open. To talk, sing, or shout, a person tightens the cords. The air breathed out makes the cords vibrate and thus produce sound. The pitch (highness or lowness) of the sound is determined by the tightness of the cords.

The voices of most adult men are deeper than those of women. This is because a man's larynx is larger than a woman's, and has longer cords. This also shows in the size of the "Adam's apple" at the front of the neck. The Adam's apple is the bulging front of the larynx, which is often visible in men because of its size, but rarely in women.

To learn to talk and sing, a person learns to change the shape and size of the opening of the mouth and throat. This changes the way the air vibrates. The person learns to stop the airflow with the lips, teeth, tongue, and epiglottis (a flap of tissue behind the base of the tongue and above the larynx). In this way, a person can form syllables, words, and other sounds that together make up speech.

LARYNX

The larynx includes the vocal cords, which vibrate when we talk or sing. The Adam's apple is a piece of cartilage that protects the front of the larynx.

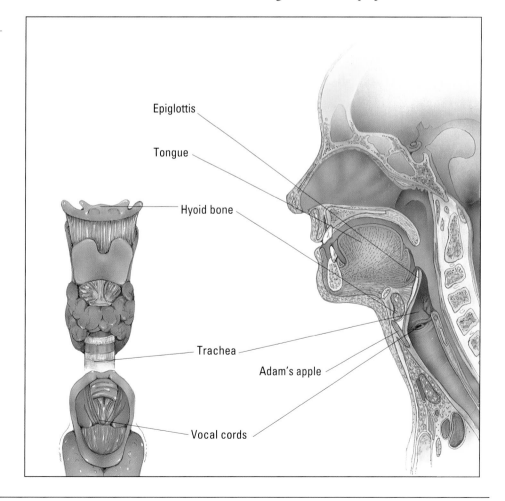

Epiglottis

Tongue

Hyoid bone

Trachea

Adam's apple

Vocal cords

LASER

The term *laser* is short for "*l*ight *a*mplification by *s*timulated *e*mission of *r*adiation." A laser is a device that sends out light beams of very high intensity. Lasers can perform a variety of tasks, such as cutting through materials, playing recorded music, reading text, and welding metal (see LIGHT; RADIATION).

Lasers are similar to other devices that give off light in that they all change energy from one form into another. However, they work in a very different way, and the type of light they produce is different. For example, in an incandescent electric light, electric current flows to a filament (wire) (see CURRENT, ELECTRIC; ELECTRIC LIGHT). The filament heats up, causing it to glow. The light given off is made up of waves of different frequencies, which radiate in many directions (see FREQUENCY; WAVE).

Lasers, on the other hand, do not produce light by heating something. Instead, a laser produces its kind of light by passing energy through atoms of a certain substance (see ATOM). The phenomenon that occurs is similar to fluorescence (see FLUORESCENCE). The atoms absorb the energy. When they do so, the electrons orbiting the nuclei are raised to a higher orbit. When the electrons fall to a lower orbit, energy is released as light. The light produced by a laser is made up of waves of the same frequency, which travel in the same direction and are practically parallel to each other. This is called coherent light. In coherent light, the light waves combine with and amplify (strengthen) each other, producing a very intense beam of light. Laser light is also highly directional. It travels in only one direction and is a narrow beam whose sides remain nearly parallel over long distances.

How lasers work All lasers include a "lasing" material. Lasing materials may be gases, liquids, or solids. Some of the most commonly used lasing materials, such as carbon dioxide and helium-argon, are gases. In a gas laser, the gas is confined in a glass tube. The inside of one end of the tube is coated completely with silver and acts like a mirror. The other end is partially coated with silver. The

tube also contains two electrodes. The electrodes are connected by wires to an energy source, such as a battery, outside the tube. Electricity flows from the battery to one electrode (see BATTERY; ELECTRICITY; ELECTRODE). Electrons move from that electrode through the gas to the other electrode. As the electrons move through the gas, they strike some of the gas atoms. This excites the gas atoms, raising their electrons to higher orbits. Eventually, the electrons drop back to their original orbits and give off the energy as light. This light strikes other atoms, which are then excited. The light may also be reflected off the silver-coated ends, exciting still more atoms.

At a certain point, the coherent light inside the tube becomes intense enough that it is able to pass out the partially silver-coated end. When this happens, the laser is said to "fire."

The first laser was made in 1960 by Theodore Maiman of the United States. Maiman's laser had a rod made of the mineral called ruby. Ruby consists of aluminum oxide and chromium oxide. One end of the rod was coated with silver and the other was partially coated. A powerful flash tube was wound

LIGHT SHOW

A laser light show (above) adds color and excitement to the performance of a rock band. Some of the laser beams can be made to switch on and off in time with the music.

Mirror

Ruby crystal

Flash tube

LASER WORKINGS

An early type of laser was based on a crystal of ruby. It produced pulses of laser light as the external flash tube flashed on and off.

Mirror with central hole

Coherent light

Laser beam

around the rod. Light from the flash tube entered the ruby and excited the chromium atoms. Light released by the atoms bounced off the silver-coated ends of the rod, hitting and exciting other chromium atoms. Eventually, all of the chromium atoms gave off light. An intense beam of red coherent light came from the end of the ruby that was not completely silvered.

Since then, many other kinds of lasers have been developed. Some lasers give a continuous beam of light. Other lasers emit light in short bursts that may last only one one-thousandth of a second.

Uses of lasers A laser can be made to give off energy at any wavelength. Some lasers produce visible light, while others produce infrared rays or ultraviolet rays (see INFRARED RAY; ULTRAVIOLET RAY). Infrared lasers are used to weld metals (see WELDING AND CUTTING). Scientists are experimenting with using ultraviolet lasers to study fusion reactions (see FUSION). In this research, several ultraviolet laser beams strike a tiny pellet of hydrogen at the same time. This causes some of the hydrogen atoms to fuse together, releasing large amounts of energy in the process.

Lasers have caused a revolution in many fields. Chemists use lasers to study the structure of atoms and molecules. Chemists also use lasers to make new compounds, to start chemical reactions, to separate elements, and to remove impurities from substances (see CHEMICAL REACTION; COMPOUND; ELEMENT; MOLECULE). Physicians use lasers to painlessly destroy surface tumors (abnormal growths). In surgery involving internal organs, physicians use lasers to cut into organs and seal off capillaries (tiny blood vessels) without damaging other tissue. Laser beams

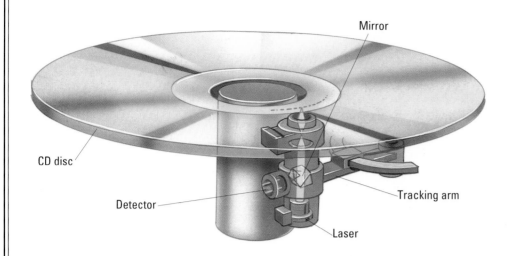

Mirror

CD disc

Detector

Tracking arm

Laser

LASER SCANNING

An audio compact disc (CD) or a CD-ROM information disc is "read" by a laser beam. The laser light reflects off the tiny pits on the underside of the disc. The reflected light bounces off a mirror into a detector, which produces varying electrical signals. Circuits convert these signals into sounds or pictures.

also can be used to repair damaged parts of the eye. Dentists are experimenting with using laser beams to remove decayed areas of a tooth. Laser beams have also been used experimentally to open clogged arteries of the heart.

Lasers are used throughout industry. Lasers can drill holes in very hard substances, such as steel and diamond. Lasers are used to weld metal parts of all sizes. For example, lasers can connect wires in a vacuum tube (see VACUUM TUBE). Producers of cardboard, plastic, and heavy fabrics use lasers to cut through stacks of large sheets quickly. The stacks of smaller sheets are then sent to manufacturers to be made into various products. Lasers are used in surveying to accurately measure distances. Lasers are aimed at a particular object. The laser light hits the object and is reflected back. The distance to the object can be measured by the amount of time it takes the laser light to return to its source. Laser light can also be used to produce three-dimensional images called holographs (see HOLOGRAPHY).

Lasers have become very important in the field of communication. Lasers can send light that can carry television and telephone signals. These signals can travel through the air, through space, or over optical fibers (see FIBER OPTICS). Lasers are used to "read" discs, known as optical discs. There are several different types. In music, a type of optical disc called a compact disc is used to store data that becomes sound. A laser converts pits and flat areas (lands) on the disc into electrical signals. These signals pass through an amplifier and loudspeaker, where they are changed into sound (see

SOUND RECORDING). Another type of optical disc, known as a CD-ROM, is used to store information and software for computers. With these, a laser inside a computer retrieves the information that has been stored in the pits and lands. This information is then manipulated by computer chips to become images, sounds, video pictures, and animated images that can be viewed on a computer or a television screen. Lasers are also used in computer printers to produce detailed images, such as letters, numbers, and artwork, quickly and accurately. The lasers "draw" the image in the form of many tiny dots on a drumlike device in the printer. Powdered ink is dusted on this image and then transferred to paper.

Lasers are used in the military. They can be bounced off a moving object, such as an airplane, to determine its distance and speed. The use of lasers to destroy enemy missiles high above the ground was proposed as part of the Strategic Defense Initiative (SDI or "Star Wars"), which was ended in 1973. Lasers are now being developed as both antisatellite and ballistic missile defense weapons as part of the Ballistic Missile Defense program in the United States.

Lasers and masers Lasers were developed from a device called a maser (see MASER). *Maser* is short for *mi*crowave *a*mplification by *s*timulated *e*mission of *r*adiation. Masers produce microwaves of just one frequency. Early lasers were sometimes called optical masers because they work on the same principle as masers.

See also MICROWAVE.

LATENT HEAT *Latent* heat means "hidden" heat. It is the heat that is gained or lost when a substance changes from one physical state to another physical state without changing temperature.

Ice (solid water) at 32°F [0°C] must be supplied with heat to melt it—that is, to turn it into liquid water. As heat is supplied, the temperature will not rise until all of the ice has melted. The heat that is gained when ice is melting is called latent heat of fusion. When all the ice has melted, more heat will raise the temperature of the liquid water. If enough heat is supplied, the liquid water will reach boiling point, 212°F [100°C]. It will start to turn to steam, a gas. However, its temperature will not rise above 212°F until all the liquid water has turned to steam at 212°F. The heat that is gained when liquid water is turning to steam is called latent heat of vaporization.

The opposite happens when something is cooled. It loses heat as it changes from gas to liquid, or from liquid to solid. Again, there is no temperature change as it becomes a liquid or a solid.
See also HEAT; STATES OF MATTER.

LATHE (lāth) A lathe is a machine that is used to give a round shape to wood, metal, or plastic. Lathes also perform the important task of cutting screw threads. The lathe, which is powered by an electric motor, spins the material to be shaped on a horizontal axis. A cutting tool is brought against the spinning material, and it cuts away the material until the desired shape is formed. The cutting tool is mounted in a special holder and can be moved in and out and from side to side.

Lathes are extremely accurate. They can perform shaping and cutting operations to within 0.0001 in. [0.0002 cm]. The most widely used kind of lathe is the center lathe, or engine lathe. Another popular kind of lathe is the turret lathe. It has six cutting tools mounted in a turret, or tool holder. This makes it possible to bring several different kinds of cutting tools into use without stopping the machine. Also, once the cutting tools have been set, the same operations can be done on piece after piece. When thousands of such operations are needed, a multiple spindle bar machine is used. It is a kind of lathe that performs six different cutting operations at once on six different pieces of material. In large, automated factories, many lathes may be run by a single computer. A person puts the material into the lathes and removes it when the work is finished. The computer takes care of the entire operation. Computer-controlled lathes are also used in small factories and precision workshops.

The idea of the lathe has been known since ancient times. It probably began with the potter's wheel. Until 1800, lathes were crude machines. Foot pedals linked to a system of belts and pulleys supplied the power that operated the lathe. These early lathes could do only a few tasks. One thing they could not do was cut screw threads. Around

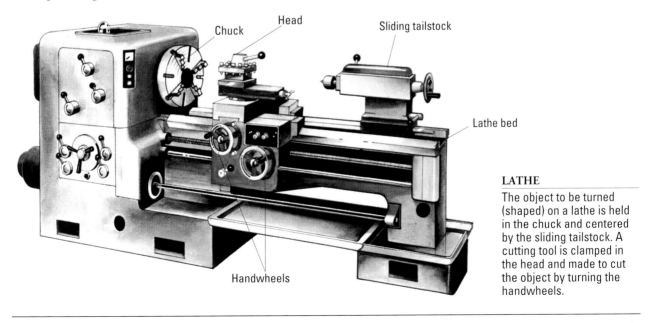

LATHE
The object to be turned (shaped) on a lathe is held in the chuck and centered by the sliding tailstock. A cutting tool is clamped in the head and made to cut the object by turning the handwheels.

1800, Henry Maudslay of England invented the first successful screw-cutting lathe. In 1873, C.M. Spencer of the United States built the first fully automatic lathe.

LATITUDE AND LONGITUDE

LATITUDE AND LONGITUDE Latitude and longitude describe positions on the earth's surface. Lines of latitude, called parallels, include the equator and the circles parallel to it. Lines of longitude, called meridians, run north and south at right angles to the parallels.

Latitude and longitude are measured in degrees (°). Each degree is divided into 60 minutes ('), and each minute is divided into 60 seconds (").

Lines of latitude

Lines of latitude Latitude is measured north and south from the equator. The equator is considered 0° latitude. There are 90 degrees of north latitude between the equator and the North Pole, and another 90 degrees of south latitude between the equator and the South Pole. Thus, the latitude at the North Pole is 90° north, while the latitude at the South Pole is 90° south.

The length of a degree of latitude ranges from 68.7 mi. [110.5 km] at the equator to 69.4 mi. [111.9 km] at the poles. This difference is due to the fact that the shape of the earth is not a perfect sphere.

Lines of longitude

Lines of longitude The prime, or first, meridian is considered 0° longitude. This line, sometimes called the Greenwich meridian, runs through Greenwich, England. There are 180 degrees of longitude both east and west from the prime meridian. The International Date Line runs along much of the 180° meridian. The length of a degree of longitude ranges from 69.17 mi. [111 km] at the equator to 0 at the poles.

See also INTERNATIONAL DATE LINE; MAP AND MAPPING.

LAUREL Laurels are a group of trees and shrubs that make up the family Lauraceae. They grow in warm areas, and most of the 2,500 or so species have tough, evergreen leaves. The family includes avocado, camphor, cinnamon, Californian myrtlewood, sassafras, and sweet bay. Some other plants are also called laurels, though they are not in the laurel family. For example, mountain laurel is a member of the heath family. Cherry laurel, widely used as a hedging plant, belongs to the rose family.

See also HEATH FAMILY; ROSE FAMILY.

LAUREL

The leaves of sweet bay, a type of laurel, can be dried and used as an herb for flavoring meat dishes.

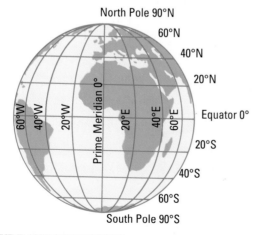

North Pole 90°N
60°N
40°N
20°N
Prime Meridian 0°
60°W 40°W 20°W 20°E 40°E 60°E
Equator 0°
20°S
40°S
60°S
South Pole 90°S

LATITUDE AND LONGITUDE

Lattitude is measured in degrees north or south of the equator (0° latitude). Longitude is measured in degrees east or west of the prime meridian (0° longitude).

LAVA Lava is molten (melted) rock that flows out of volcanoes or from cracks in the earth. While the rock is still underground, it is called magma (see MAGMA; VOLCANO). The temperature of red-hot lava ranges from 1,300 to 2,200°F [700 to 1,200°C].

There are different kinds of lava. Acidic lava has a high content of silica, making it very thick and

LAVA

Flowing lava often starts dangerous fires and can even set fire to the tar on roads (right). Once lava has cooled and set, the solid rock formed often shows patterns of ripples (below).

slow moving. Acidic lava usually hardens before it travels very far. It is blocky in appearance and is sometimes called blocky lava. Basic lava is so fluid that it may flow for miles before becoming solid. It is ropey in appearance and is sometimes called ropey lava.

Lava may contain large amounts of gases. These gases often cause explosions within the volcano. Sometimes, the gases form bubbles in the lava. If this happens, a kind of rock called pumice forms (see PUMICE).

When lava dries quickly, it may form large amounts of natural glass. After the dried lava is broken down, it becomes fertile land for growing crops.

Lava that flows from fissures (cracks) in the earth may build up sheets of lava called lava beds. The Columbia Plateau in the northwestern United States is a lava bed 5,000 ft. [1,500 m] thick in some places. The Hawaiian Islands are made up mostly of lava.

LAVENDER The lavenders are small evergreen shrubs belonging to the mint family, Labiatae (see EVERGREEN; MINT FAMILY). There are over 20 species, and most of them grow in the Mediterranean area. Several are cultivated in gardens. The common lavender may reach a height of 4 ft. [120 cm]. It has narrow, grayish green leaves and spikes of light purple flowers growing in whorls around the tops of the stems. The flowers and leaves smell as they do because of the oil produced by tiny glands located among the tiny hairs covering the entire plant.

The word *lavender* comes from the Latin word meaning "to wash." It is so named because the ancient Romans used to put the sweet-smelling flowers into their bath water. Today, the oil produced by several lavender species is used to make perfumes and other cosmetics.

LAVENDER

Lavender is grown commercially for its fragrant flowers, which are used to make perfume.

ANTOINE LAVOISIER
Antoine Lavoisier founded modern chemistry. He was the first to correctly explain what happens during combustion.

LAVOISIER, ANTOINE (lä vwä′ zē ā′, än twăn′) (1743–1794)

Antoine Lavoisier was a French chemist. He was born in Paris and first became a lawyer. He worked as a tax collector and did scientific research in his spare time. He made so many important discoveries that he is called "the father of modern chemistry."

In 1766, Lavoisier won a gold medal for his idea on how to light the streets of Paris. He was later given the job of gunpowder officer. Lavoisier did a great deal of research on combustion (burning). In 1772, he showed that the ash from burnt metals is heavier than the original metals. Until this discovery, people thought that substances gave off something called phlogiston when they burned. Lavoisier showed that, in fact, something was added. After Joseph Priestley discovered oxygen in 1774, Lavoisier stated that air contains two gases (see PRIESTLEY, JOSEPH). He said the one called oxygen helped combustion and breathing. The other gas did not. He called the second gas azote. It is now called nitrogen.

Lavoisier made other discoveries. He determined what a chemical reaction really is. His system of naming chemical compounds is still used today. He recorded all his discoveries in a textbook called *Elementary Treatise on Chemistry*. This book contained the first published table of chemical elements. After the French Revolution of 1789, Lavoisier was willing to help the government. However, because of his political ideas and the fact that he had been a tax collector, he was put to death by guillotine.

LAWRENCE, ERNEST (1901–1958)

Ernest Orlando Lawrence was an American physicist. He studied atomic physics at the University of California. Lawrence was one of the scientists who tried to discover what atoms are made of. To do this, he tried to split atoms by bombarding them with hydrogen ions (see ATOMS; IONS AND IONIZATION). The machines then available for producing a stream of ions used a very large electric field to make them move swiftly. As a result, they were called accelerators.

Lawrence invented a machine called a cyclotron. This sent the ions around and around in a spiral, giving them extra energy on each pass. This very powerful accelerator enabled great discoveries to be made in atomic physics. Lawrence won the Nobel Prize in 1939 for this invention. The element lawrencium is named for him.

See also ACCELERATORS, PARTICLE.

LAXATIVE

A laxative is a drug or other substance that helps relieve constipation. Constipation is a condition in which feces (solid body wastes) become hardened, making it difficult to empty the intestines regularly (see DIGESTION). There are various types of laxatives, which act in different ways. Some drugs act as stimulants to the intestines. As a result of taking these drugs, water and salts accumulate in the intestines, and peristaltic contractions (the squeezing actions that push food through the digestive system) occur more frequently. These drugs include phenolphthalein and castor oil. Mineral oils make it easier for feces to move through the intestines, because the oil softens the feces. However, frequent use of this drug may prevent absorption of fat-soluble vitamins, such as vitamins A and E (see VITAMIN). Other kinds of laxatives increase the bulk of the feces, again making them pass through the intestines more easily. Examples are bran and psyllium. Still another kind of laxative is called an osmotic agent. This kind of drug causes a great deal of water to be retained in the feces, so they become loose and pass quickly. These drugs include epsom salt (magnesium sulfate), glycerin, and sorbitol.

Laxatives should be used with great care and never for a long period of time. Almost all laxatives can become habit-forming and may prevent the absorption of nutrients from the intestines. The best way to prevent constipation is to include high-fiber foods in the diet (see DIET). Such foods include raw fruits and vegetables, and whole-grain breads and cereals.

See also INTESTINE.

LCD (LIQUID CRYSTAL DISPLAY) An

LCD is an electronic device that shows letters or numbers on a panel. LCDs are used in certain calculators, computers, and watches (see CALCULTOR; CLOCK AND WATCH; COMPUTER; ELECTRONICS).

An LCD has an organic (carbon-containing) substance called a liquid crystal. Between a certain range of temperatures, liquid crystal flows like a liquid, yet its atoms arrange themselves like the atoms of solid crystals. The atoms form a definite molecular pattern (see ATOM; CRYSTAL; MOLECULE). Liquid crystals have the ability to twist polarized light (see POLARIZED LIGHT). Polarized light is orderly waves of light that vibrate in one direction only.

LCDs consist of several basic parts—liquid crystal, glass sheets, electrical conductors, polarizing filters, and a reflector. The liquid crystal is spread as a thin film between two glass sheets. The glass sheets are only about 0.0005 in. [0.012 mm] apart. The inner surfaces of the glass sheets are coated with patterns of a substance that conducts electricity and is nearly transparent (see-through). The patterns, which are vertical and horizontal bars, are used to represent letters or numbers. The bars are connected to electrical conductors at the edges of the glass (see CONDUCTION OF ELECTRICITY). The glass sheets are sandwiched between two polarizing filters. Behind the rear filter is a reflector.

In an LCD, ordinary light passes through the front filter and is changed into polarized light that vibrates in a horizontal direction. If there is no electrical current passing from an electrical conductor to a particular bar in the pattern, the liquid crystals near that bar twist the polarized light. The polarized light, which is now vertical, can pass through the rear filter. There, the polarized light bounces off the reflector and passes back through the rear filter. The liquid crystals then twist the light so it can pass through the horizontal front filter. This makes the appropriate portion of the panel appear light. However, a different effect occurs if electric current passes through to a particular bar. The liquid crystals near that bar do not twist the polarized light. The polarized light continues to head in a horizontal direction and is blocked by the rear filter. Because no light is reflected and passes back through, that particular bar appears dark. These two effects occur at the same time so that the bars form letters or numbers. In a calculator or computer, pressing a key causes certain bars to be electrically charged. In a watch, the movement causes certain bars to be electrically charged.

An advantage of an LCD is that it does not need a light source; it uses available light. This means that an LCD uses very little electricity. Devices with LCDs often come with a small light source so that the LCD can be read when there is little or no available light.

LCD

LCDs—liquid crystal displays—are used in digital watches, pocket calculators, and, as here, in personal organizers.

In another kind of LCD, liquid-crystal dyes instead of polarizing filters are used. A color change occurs when the patterns are electrically charged. LCDs are gradually being replaced by other display devices, including plasma and flat panel electroluminescent displays, that produce letters and numbers that are sharper and that appear in color.

LEACHING *Leaching* is a term that can refer to a process in which minerals are dissolved or washed out of soil. It takes place mostly in areas with plentiful rainfall. Rainwater enters the soil and carries dissolved minerals below the roots of most plants. Thus, the plants do not get the nutrients they need. In some cases, the water removes the minerals completely from the soil. Sometimes leached minerals are carried to the soil surface by an upward movement of water.

Another use of the term *leaching* is in a leaching field, which is an underground area of fine sand and gravel that catches the overflow of sewage from waste tanks called septic tanks. *Leaching* is also a term used in chemistry. It is a means by which a liquid is passed through a substance that takes out some of the elements of that liquid.

LEAD Lead is a dense, soft, gray metallic element. The chemical symbol for lead is Pb. *Pb* is short for the Latin word for lead, *plumbum*. Lead has the atomic number of 82 and a relative atomic mass of 207.19. Lead is one of the heaviest metals. The main source of lead is the mineral galena (see ELEMENT; GALENA; METAL AND METALLURGY). Because lead is so soft, it can be beaten, cut, and shaped easily. Lead does not rust, so it has been used for thousands of years to make water pipes. However, because lead is poisonous, other metals and plastics are now preferred for pipes that carry drinking water.

Lead's denseness allows it to absorb radiation. For example, walls in nuclear power plants and containers that hold radioactive materials are lined with lead (see RADIATION; RADIOACTIVITY). People who have X rays taken of their teeth or other body parts are placed under lead blankets. These blankets protect the rest of the body from the radiation.

The X-ray technician may also stand behind a lead-lined wall (see X RAY).

Lead also has a low melting point. It melts at 621.1°F [327.3°C]. It is sometimes added to other metals to form alloys that can be melted easily (see ALLOY). Solder can be made this way. Solder is used to bond two metals together (see SOLDERING AND BRAZING). Pewter is made of tin and lead.

Useful lead compounds made in industry include plumbous oxide (PbO) and lead dioxide (PbO_2) (see COMPOUND). Plumbous oxide is used in making certain kinds of glass and ceramics. Lead dioxide is used in automobile batteries. Other lead compounds were once used to make the red, yellow, and orange pigments for paints (see PIGMENT). However, because lead is poisonous, its use has been restricted in paints. For example, it can no longer be used in house paints or paints for household objects, such as toys. Old buildings or old toys may still be coated with paints containing lead. It is important that children do not eat paint chips or chew or suck on objects that may contain lead. Lead compounds have also been used as an additive to gasoline (see GASOLINE). However, these compounds release poisonous fumes when they are burned in an automobile. Lead has since been phased out of most gasoline.

LEAD
The principal ore of lead is galena (above), which consists mainly of lead sulfide. It may also contain useful amounts of silver. The lead water pipe (right) was made by the ancient Romans. The Roman (Latin) word for lead is *plumbum*, which gives us our words *plumber* and *plumbing*.

A leaf is the part of a plant where most of the plant's food is made by photosynthesis (see PHOTO-SYNTHESIS). Most leaves are green because many of their cells contain chlorophyll (see CELL; CHORO-PHYLL). The food produced in the leaves is carried to other parts of the plant for storage. This process is called translocation. The plant uses its stored food for energy needed for growth and other processes. This food is also an important part of the food chain (see FOOD CHAIN).

External structure Although leaves differ much in appearance, most have a blade and petiole, and some have stipules. The blade is usually large, broad, and flattened. It contains large numbers of chloroplasts, which are chlorophyll-containing structures within the cells. The blade usually has several veins. The veins carry food (sugar) from, and water to, the leaf. They also act as skeletons, giving the blade support and form (see VASCULAR PLANT).

The petiole is the stalk of the leaf, connecting it to a twig. The petiole contains many tiny tubelike structures that lead from the xylem and phloem of the stem to the veins of the blade (see PHLOEM; XYLEM). Some leaves have no petiole and are said to be sessile—that is, without stalks.

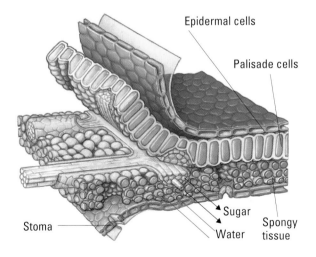

Epidermal cells
Palisade cells
Stoma
Sugar
Water
Spongy tissue

LEAF STRUCTURE

The upper part of a leaf consists of epidermal cells. A similar layer covers the underside of the leaf. It contains holes called stomata (plural of *stoma*) that allow gases (carbon dioxide and oxygen) to pass in and out of the leaf. Palisade cells contain chloroplasts, in which photosynthesis takes place.

The stipules are usually tiny, leaflike structures located at the base of the petiole but they are not present on all leaves.

Types of leaves Leaves may be simple or compound. A simple leaf has an undivided blade. A compound leaf is broken up into several leaflets. The leaflets are usually found on both sides of a central stalk called the rachis. They may, however, fan out from the petiole. The outer margin of the leaf blade or the leaflets may be smooth or may be toothed (with small, jagged points) or lobed (with larger, more widely separated points).

Leaves are arranged on a stem in such a way that they receive the maximum amount of sunlight. When looked at from above, the leaves form a sort of mosaic, but they are not all arranged in the same way. The most common arrangement, known as the opposite system, is for the leaves to grow in pairs from each side of each node (see NODE). In the alternate system, only one leaf grows from each node or joint on the stem, but each leaf is on the opposite side of the stem from the leaves immediately above and below it. Spirally arranged leaves also grow singly, but they spiral up the stem like a spiral staircase. When three or more leaves spring from a single node, the arrangement is known as whorled, but this is quite rare. In a rosette, the leaves all spring from more or less the same point on the stem, and they often overlap each other to some extent. This arrangement is most commonly seen in the leaves right at the base of the plant.

The veins in leaves also have special arrangements. In parallel venation (veining), the veins extend the length of the leaf without branching, although they may be linked by fine connections. This arrangement is present in monocotyledons (one seed-leaf plants). Most dicotyledons (two seed-leaves plants) show one of two kinds of net venation, in which the veins form a netlike pattern. The two kinds of net venation are pinnate and palmate. In pinnate venation, there is one main vein with smaller veins branching off. In palmate venation, there are several large veins that spread from the base of the leaflike fingers from the palm of the hand. Smaller veins branch off from each of the larger veins.

Internal structure

A leaf is made of several layers of cells. One layer, called the upper epidermis, covers the top surface of the leaf. The lower epidermis covers the underside of the leaf. The epidermal cells are clear so that light can pass through to the inner cells. The upper and lower epidermis protect these delicate inner cells.

Just below the upper epidermis is the palisade tissue. It is made of densely packed, rectangular cells that contain many chloroplasts. Most of the photosynthesis takes place in the palisade tissue. Between the palisade tissue and the lower epidermis is the spongy tissue. This is made of loosely packed cells of irregular shapes. Most of the water that evaporates from the leaf does so from the spongy tissue.

The lower epidermis has many valvelike openings called stomata (see STOMA). Each stoma is surrounded by two sausage-shaped guard cells that control the size of the opening. The stomata allow the movement of air in and out of a leaf. Carbon dioxide in the air that enters a leaf is used in photosynthesis. Oxygen, a waste product of photosynthesis, is in the air that moves out of the leaf. Water vapor is lost in the air moving out through the stomata. This loss of water vapor is called transpiration, and it causes a constant movement of water from the roots to the leaves (see TRANSPIRATION). The stomata are usually closed at night, when photosynthesis is not occurring. This helps slow the rate of transpiration and thus save water. The stomata are usually open during the day to allow the entry of air containing carbon dioxide for use in photosynthesis.

The upper surface of the leaf is often covered with a waxy cuticle produced by the epidermal cells. The cuticle protects the leaf from very hot or very cold weather and from insects. It also helps lessen the evaporation of water through the epidermis. A thinner cuticle is sometimes present on the underside of the leaf. Some leaves have tiny hairs growing from the epidermis through the cuticle.

These hairs also help to protect the leaves and to reduce water loss.

Differences in leaves

The number of leaves on a plant varies from one to several million, depending on the species. The leaves themselves are of many different sizes and shapes. The largest leaves are those of an African raffia palm, and measure 50 ft. [15 m] long. The smallest are from a type of duckweed. They measure less than 0.04 in. [1 mm] across.

The leaves of many conifers—such as pine trees—are called needles (see CONIFER). They are very narrow and pointed and often fan out from the twig in all directions. Some leaves are like scales, to protect buds and other parts. Bracts are scalelike leaves that grow just below the blossoms of some flowers. Their job is mostly to protect. Some bracts, however, are brightly colored and may be taken for the blossom itself. A spathe is a special leaf that surrounds and protects a flower. It often serves to keep

Simple leaves

Linear (grass) Ovate (pear)

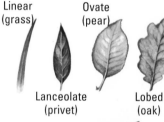

Lanceolate (privet) Lobed (oak) Peltate (nasturtium) Lobed palmate (castor bean)

Compound leaves

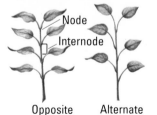

Palmate (horse chestnut) Pinnate (mountain ash) Pinnate (twice) (honey locust)

Arrangements of leaves

Node
Internode

Rosette

Opposite Alternate Whorled or spiral

TYPES OF LEAVES

The shape of leaves and the way they are arranged on the stem often characterize a plant. The top row shows examples of simple leaf shapes. The second row illustrates compound leaves. Either type can be arranged on the stem in any of the ways shown in the last row.

LEAF VARIETY

The leaves of the salvia (top left) can be used as a flavoring herb, better known as sage. The water lily's leaves (top center) float and provide shelter for small aquatic creatures. The coleus (top right) is valued as a house plant for its multicolored leaves. The agave (left) has thick-skinned leaves to conserve water in the dry deserts where it grows.

the reproductive structures warm in cooler climates and at night. Some leaves are formed as spines or prickles. Most of these have lost their food producing ability and instead serve to protect the plant from animals. The leaves of some plants are used to catch insects (see CARNIVOROUS PLANT).

Some plants are called evergreens because they always have some leaves (see EVERGREEN). These leaves do not live forever, however. They die a few at a time, and others grow in their place. As a result, these plants have green leaves year-round. Deciduous trees lose their leaves in the fall and grow new ones in the spring (see DECIDUOUS TREE). These leaves often change to reds, yellows, or oranges before dying. This is caused by the breakdown of chlorophyll in the cells. The chlorophyll begins to break down when a layer of cork forms across the base of the petiole, cutting off the supply of water. When the water is cut off, photosynthesis stops, and the chlorophyll breaks down. As the green chlorophyll begins to disappear, other pigments in the leaf cells begin to show through (see PIGMENT). Some of the common pigments are xanthophyll (yellow), carotene (orange), and anthocyanin (red). Although these colors are present throughout the year, they are usually hidden by the much greater amounts of chlorophyll.

See also CHROMOPLAST.　　　PROJECT 61, 68, 69

LEAF INSECT A leaf insect is any of a number of species of large plant-eating insects belonging to the order Phasmida. They are sometimes called walking leaves because they look so much like leaves (see CAMOUFLAGE; PROTECTIVE COLORATION).

The body and legs of leaf insects are broadly flattened. The wings are large and ribbed, like leaves, and they lie flat on the back. These insects may even have tiny, leaflike growths on their legs. They feed at night and rest quietly among shrubs and leaves during the day. Leaf insects are found mostly in warm areas, especially in East Asia and the nearby islands.

See also INSECT.

LEAF INSECT
A leaf insect's remarkable resemblance to a leaf makes it hard to spot on plants.

LEAKEY FAMILY Leakey is the family name of three famous anthropologists: a husband and wife and their son. They made important discoveries in Africa about the origins of human beings.

Leakey, Louis S.B. (1903–1972) Louis Leakey was born in Kenya, Africa. His parents were British missionaries. Leakey was an archeologist and anthropologist. He and his wife, Mary, were working in Kenya in the early 1960s when they discovered fossils of a humanlike creature who lived 14 million years ago (see FOSSIL). They called this creature *Kenyapithecus.*

The Leakeys also discovered a humanlike skull at Olduvai Gorge in Tanzania that proved to be about 1.7 million years old. The skull belonged to a more advanced humanlike creature that anthropologists call *Australopithecus* (see HUMAN BEING). The Leakeys found other, even more advanced fossils in the same area. Based on this evidence, Leakey claimed that two humanlike species—one primitive, one fairly advanced—lived in the same area at the same time. This theory was generally rejected until it was confirmed in 1972 by the Leakeys' son, Richard.

LEAKEY FAMILY
Louis Leakey and Mary Leakey are shown with one of the fossil skulls they discovered in Africa.

Leakey, Mary Douglas (1913–) Anthropologist Mary Leakey worked alongside her husband, Louis, and was responsible for many of the fossil finds at Olduvai Gorge in Tanzania, including the skull of *Australopithecus.* One of her most significant discoveries, made in 1978, was the footprints of humanlike creatures preserved in fossilized volcanic ash near Olduvai Gorge. The footprints date from 4.5 million years ago. Mary Leakey and her son continue to search for remains of humankind's earliest ancestors.

Leakey, Richard E.F. (1944–) Anthropologist Richard Leakey is the son of Louis and Mary Leakey. In 1972, Leakey discovered a fossil skull in Kenya that is about 2 million years old and had a much larger brain than *Australopithecus.* Anthropologists refer to it as *Homo habilis* and consider it the first human being because of its larger brain, certain dental features, and the presence of tools associated with it. This find confirmed Louis Leakey's theory that two humanlike species lived in Africa about 2 million years ago.

See also ANTHROPOLOGY; ARCHEOLOGY; EVOLUTION.

LEARNING AND MEMORY

The study of learning is one of the most important fields in psychology, which is the science of behavior (see PSYCHOLOGY). Scientists have been working many years to discover just what learning is. The most accepted answer is that learning is a process by which past experience is used to determine behavior. Behavior includes actions, feelings, thoughts, and responses to physical sensations.

Learning may help change future behavior. Almost all human behavior is learned. Even very simple animals can learn things. Learning takes place all the time. However, there is no easy way to explain how this happens. Psychologists have described four kinds of learning. Classical conditioning is perhaps the simplest kind of learning. Ivan Pavlov, a Russian physiologist, first described it during the early 1900s. Pavlov offered a dog some food and at the same time rang a bell. The sight of food made the dog's mouth water. Pavlov called this an unconditioned response because it was automatic and not learned. Soon, however, ringing the bell, without offering food, was enough to cause the dog's mouth to water. Pavlov called this a conditioned response. The dog had "learned" to salivate in response to the bell. A conditioned response had become fixed to a new stimulus, or cause (the bell). To indicate the fact that a stimulus brings a response in this kind of learning, classical conditioning is often called respondent learning (see PAVLOV, IVAN PETROVICH).

Another form of learning is called instrumental learning. Often a person learns to do a behavior as a result of what happens after the person does it. For example, a child may learn to ask for a treat. There is no stimulus that causes the response of asking. The child asks simply because he or she has learned that such behavior may get him or her a treat. The treat is known as the reinforcer; it is a reward that causes the child to ask again. Instrumental conditioning is also called operant conditioning. The learned response operates, or works, on the environment to produce some effect.

Multiple-response learning is a kind of learning

LEARNING TO READ

Children acquire nearly half of their adult reading vocabulary in the first ten years after first learning to read.

LEARNING TO BALANCE
A pair of small additional wheels, called training wheels, allow a small child to ride a bicycle. Once the child has learned how to balance, the training wheels can be removed.

that happens when a skill is learned. A sequence (order) of simple things must first be learned in order to learn the skill. Using a computer keyboard is one kind of multiple-response learning. At first, a person has to type letter by letter. With practice, the person learns to type word by word, or phrase by phrase. Other examples include learning such things as a poem or another language, in which a person must learn a sequence of words.

Insight learning involves solving a problem through understanding how the different parts of a problem fit together. A simple example is that of a young child wanting to climb on top of a table. The child may decide to use a stool to get onto a chair, and then use the chair to climb onto the table.

Whenever a creature repeats an action it has learned, the "knowledge" of how to do it—whether the creature is aware of it or not—must have been stored inside the creature in some way. This storage is called memory. Memory is the ability to recall things that have happened in the past. Memory is part of learning. One needs memory to ride a bicycle. A dog needs to remember if it is to come when called.

Memory is said to be stored in the brain as a "memory trace." How this works is not entirely understood. Some scientists believe that certain chemical substances carried by nerves, and other chemicals circulating in the blood as hormones, may be involved in learning and the development and storage of new memories (see HORMONE; NERVOUS SYSTEM).

Other research into memory uses psychological

techniques to understand how the brain works. Psychologists use three methods to find out how a person remembers. For example, using the method of recall, the researcher might give a person a grocery list. The person is asked to memorize the list, then put it away. The most natural way to find out how much the person remembers of the grocery list is to ask what he or she remembers. Another method is called recognition. The researcher might give the person another grocery list that has some items from the first list and some new items. The person is asked to differentiate between the two kinds of items. Often the person will be able to recognize items from the first list that he or she cannot otherwise recall. A third method of finding how much a person remembers is called relearning. Here the person is asked to read over the first list again. The person will probably learn the list faster the second time than he or she did the first time. The difference in the time it takes to relearn the list is thought to be a measure of how much a person has remembered.

One way of remembering something is to repeat it many times. Interest is very important. Boring lists of facts are much more difficult to remember than something that a person is interested in. Motivation, or wanting to do something, is also important. Motivation is linked with reward—this is what psychologists call reinforcement. For example, a hungry animal quickly learns how to do something if that action gets the animal food. For humans, wanting to learn is often motivation. The praise of a teacher or the knowledge that an answer is correct are rewarding.

Many memories are not kept very long. For example, a telephone number that you have just looked up is stored only in short-term memory. After a short amount of time, some information may be carried to the "permanent" memory, also known as long-term memory. A blow on the head, or some kind of shock, may stop this process. For example, a person in an accident may not be able to remember what happened just before the accident. Loss of memory is called amnesia.

See also BEHAVIOR OF ANIMALS; BRAIN; INSTINCT; SKINNER, BURRHUS FREDERIC.

LEARNING DISORDER Learning disorders are disabilities that interfere with a child's ability to learn. Learning disorders can interfere with concentration, language, memory, or coordination. Children with learning disorders often do poorly in school. Learning disorders are not related to intelligence or to impaired vision or hearing. Children with learning disorders may have average to above-average intelligence and are as likely to have normal hearing and vision as other children.

Learning disorders may be caused by a chemical imbalance in the body or by damage to the brain or nerves. The damage may come from injury, such as a sharp blow to the head; from a lack of oxygen during birth; or from exposure to certain chemicals, such as lead in paint. Learning disorders also can result from poor nutrition in a pregnant woman or a lack of learning experiences during early childhood. Some disorders may also be linked to heredity or emotional problems.

There are many kinds of learning disorders. Learning disorders may be perceptual. This means that a child's ability to organize and interpret verbal messages is affected. For example, the child may not be able to tell when one word ends in a sentence and another word begins. Perceptual disorders can interfere with the development of language skills. For example, dyslexia affects the ability to understand spoken or written words. Children with auditory dyslexia have difficulty remembering sounds and applying them to letters they read. Children with visual dyslexia reverse words or letters and have difficulty remembering the order of letters in a word. For example, the letter *b* might be read as the letter *d*. The word *saw* might be read as the word *was*.

Learning disorders also can interfere with behavior. For example, children who are hyperactive cannot sit still and may become impatient and boisterous. A child with the learning disorder called emotional lability experiences unexplained mood changes. This makes it difficult for the child to concentrate. It may also affect the child's willingness to participate in learning activities. Orientation-related disorders affect a child's sense of direction. For example, a child may be a poor reader because he or she cannot tell the difference between right and left or up and down.

Some learning disorders involve lack of muscle control. Dyspraxia is the inability to properly move parts of the body involved in speech, such as the tongue. This interferes with the ability to ask questions and to repeat information. In dysgraphia, the eyes and hands do not work together smoothly, resulting in poor handwriting. Poor handwriting interferes with writing exercises and the child's ability to take notes.

In the United States, 5 to 10 percent of all children between the ages of five and seventeen have one or more learning disorders. These disorders may continue into adulthood unless help is received.

Diagnosis of whether a child has a learning disorder involves several steps. A child who has obvious difficulties learning and behaving may be given a series of written and visual tests to determine the cause of these difficulties. These tests may be given by the special education department at the child's school. The child may also be examined by a psychiatrist or other physician to determine if there is a physical or psychological reason behind the learning difficulties.

There are several ways to treat learning disorders. Treatment may involve changes in how the child is taught. For example, a child who has a perceptual learning disorder may be taught by manipulating objects or looking at pictures rather than reading and writing words. The child may be placed in a class with children with similar learning disorders. A child whose learning disorder stems from emotional problems may undergo counseling. If the learning disorder is linked to a physical problem, specialists try to correct the problem. For example, the child may be placed on a special diet.

LED (LIGHT-EMITTING DIODE) An LED is a device for producing light from an electric current. It depends upon the special properties of substances called semiconductors. A semiconductor is a substance that has different resistances to the passage of an electric current under different circumstances (see CURRENT, ELECTRIC; SEMICONDUCTOR).

When an electric current flows through the junction between two different kinds of semiconductors, electrons are gained by one side and lost by the other. Electrons jump from one atom to another to fill the "holes" left by missing electrons.

In an LED, electrons with high energy jump to fill the holes left by low-energy electrons. This means that there is some energy left over. The energy is given out by the atoms as light energy. Each time an electron jumps, a photon of light energy is emitted. The light is given out by the atoms near the junction between the semiconductors (see PHOTON).

The wavelength of the light emitted depends on the kinds of atoms in the semiconductors. The useful wavelengths are those of red, orange, green, and yellow light. The light that is emitted can be used in several ways. It can be used to show glowing numbers or letters in different instruments. Many digital watches, calculators, clocks, scales, and cash registers use LEDs. Unlike the light given out by an electric light bulb, the light from an LED is "cold." None of the electrical energy is wasted as heat. LEDs are also used in communication. They produce light signals that are passed along by means of fiber optics.

See also FIBER OPTICS; LCD.

LED

A pocket light powered by an LED, or a light-emitting diode, is pictured above. LEDs are devices made with semiconductors that emit light when an electric current passes through them.

TSUNG DAO LEE

Tsung Dao Lee shared the 1957 Nobel Prize for physics with a fellow Chinese-American physicist, for disproving the law of parity for certain nuclear reactions.

LEE, TSUNG DAO (1926–) (lē, dzōŏng dou) Tsung Dao Lee is a Chinese-American physicist. Lee is best known for his work with Chen Ning Yang and Chien-shiung Wu (see WU, CHIEN-SHIUNG; YANG, CHEN NING).

With Yang, Lee developed a theory that suggested that a long accepted law of physics was not always true (see PHYSICS). This law, called the law of conservation of parity, says there is no way to tell whether something is an event or a mirror image of the event because both satisfy laws of nature.

However, Lee and Yang said that there is a difference between the event and the image in certain nuclear reactions. Wu performed the actual experiment that proved their theory in 1957. Lee and Yang were awarded the Nobel Prize for physics in 1957.

Lee was born in China. After attending college there he came to the United States and attended the University of Chicago. There, he worked with Enrico Fermi and received a doctoral degree in physics (see FERMI, ENRICO). Lee then taught physics at the University of California at Berkeley. In 1951, he was offered membership at the Institute for Advanced Study in Princeton, New Jersey. The Institute is a research center for those scientists who have already received a doctoral degree.

In 1953, Lee began teaching physics at Columbia University in New York City. While at Columbia, Lee began the work with Yang that would earn them the Nobel Prize. He was made a member of the National Academy of Sciences in 1964. The academy conducts scientific research and also advises the government about scientific matters.